From
PLANT
To
PLANET

Nudge your way towards healthier, more sustainable food habits

VIVIENNE ALEXA ROBINSON | POORNIMA LUTHRA

FOREWORD BY VIKAS GARG, Founder and CEO of *abillion*

From Plant to Planet: Nudge Your Way Towards Healthier, More Sustainable Food Habits

1st edition, September 2021
Copyright © Vivienne Alexa Robinson & Poornima Luthra

Authors: Vivienne Alexa Robinson & Poornima Luthra
Book coach: Malene Bendtsen (www.malenebendtsen.com)
Editor: Dina Honour (www.dinahonour.com)
Book design: Diren Yardimli

ISBN Hardback: 978-87-972903-1-6

To continue your journey as a Plantier, please visit:
plantier.earth
instagram.com/beaplantier
facebook.com/beaplantier
linkedin.com/in/beaplantier

Contents

CONTENTS

CONTENTS

In it Together

Foreword by Vikas Garg, Founder & CEO of abillion

*M*any of our friends say that my wife Sonia's pulled pork sandwiches are the best they've ever had. That makes me proud for two reasons. One, I love cooking for people. I love how you can communicate warmth and sincerity through hospitality; it's also why I admire chefs and restaurateurs so much. Second, our pulled pork sandwiches have no pork in them. They're entirely plant-based, with jackfruit as the hero ingredient. So when my raging carnivore friends rave about this dish I'm thrilled, because I know I'm about to convert someone to the idea that plant-based food can be incredibly satisfying.

For many years, vegan food had a bad rap. Pundits and critics called it "bird seed" or "rabbit food". They promoted the idea that vegan food would be tasteless or unpalatable bowls of greens, often raw and tossed together, topped with tofu and sprinkled with seeds. That couldn't be further from the truth. Vegan food can take any number of forms and come from any number of cuisines from around the world. What vegan cookery needs are champions. The great thing is that today, influence can come not just from celebrity chefs and food writers, but also digital media savvy plant-based foodies and home cooks. Vivienne and Poornima have stepped up, put on the capes and have become, in my book at least, the kind of champions that we need.

From Plant to Planet is a great cookbook. It is filled with over 50 delicious recipes, many of which I plan to prepare and share with loved ones. But this book is so much more than just a cookbook. It is a work of love and passion that informs and educates us on how to habitually make sustainable choices. This resonates so much with me because it is the same mission that inspired me to start abillion.

Being vegan is so much more than just diet, though that is the most immediate entry point for many. To me, it has become such a fundamental part of who I am and informs every conscious decision I make — from the clothes and products I wear, to the brands and places that inspire me. Choosing to take into consideration animal life, our planet's ecosystem, and each other is something that can be learnt, and this wonderful book is a great primer on training oneself to be more mindful and conscious. And eventually, become what the authors call a "plantier".

I am so pleased to see this book come to life and congratulate Vivienne and Poornima on its release. I hope you take as much from reading this as I did and the authors have in putting it together.

Vikas Garg
Founder & CEO of abillion

A Little Note

From Us to You

*C*ongratulations, and welcome on a journey towards health and sustainability! If you're reading this book, you've joined a community of people around the world who are looking for ways to eat better – both for the planet and for their own health. Our relationship with food is often a complicated one. Food is not just for sustenance; and we all have our own personal dynamic with food that is often influenced by a complex web of our prior experiences and understanding. Our food choices reflect our lifestyle, stage of life, personal preferences, intolerances and allergies, the people we live with and importantly, our emotions. These factors all make changing our food habits extremely challenging.

With growing, credible research showing that there is a real need for us to shift towards more sustainable food choices, many of us are wondering how and where to begin. Sometimes the information out there can be so overwhelming that we end up more confused than when we began. We're often confronted with new research and evidence, sometimes with differing viewpoints. From both environmental and health standpoints, there is a lot to grasp. While it can seem contradictory, the phrase *'What is good for us is good for the planet'* might make things easier to understand. It's this simple but effective philosophy that underpins our book, and one that we will continue to come back to as we help distill the information out there. We'll introduce you to the idea of viewing our "gut" health as a rainforest, inhabited by thousands of species, all living symbiotically. As the global community has moved away from eating sustainably, we're experiencing deforestation of both, the rainforests within our bodies and those outside of them. We believe that we can restore and protect this delicate balance through eating a diverse and plant-rich diet.

We're not environmentalists or doctors. We're just like you, two humans looking to make our planet more sustainable and our bodies healthier. We want to share what we've learnt along our journeys, the knowledge we've acquired through the credentials we have worked towards gaining, and the experiences we've had. We know the challenges faced when you are transforming your food habits because we've been through them ourselves.

We wrote this book during the COVID-19 lockdowns of 2020 and 2021 while based in two different countries. Thank goodness for technology! We were able to stay connected through video calls and we both became familiar with our iPhones and SLR cameras. In fact, we used them to take photos of the dishes in our recipes, which we've included in this book. During the first lockdown in 2020, many people spent time reflecting on their lifestyle choices. Some were looking for ways to be more sustainable and healthier. With restaurants closed, we found that many of our clients and friends were reaching out to us for ideas on plant-based meals to cook at home. That was all the motivation we needed. Together we wrote this book to serve as a guide towards practising more planet-friendly, body-friendly food habits by incorporating simple, but delicious plant-based meals.

Through 5 nudges, our goal is to help shape your understanding, attitude and behaviours towards sustainable food habits and give you the tools and recipes to enjoy more plant-based meals. We share practical tips to make the process of including plant-based meals easier and enjoyable. The recipes that we share are our family favourites. They are the tried and true meals that we cook on busy weeknights, rushed school days, and lazy Sunday mornings. They are the meals we cook often, using simple, fresh ingredients. We kept them unfussy to make your journey easier. These meals are delicious and substantial, whilst being planet-friendly. They are influenced by the food of nations where plant-based cooking is part of daily food practices – China, India, Thailand, Mexico, Japan, Italy and Morocco among others.

We believe that a journey towards sustainability is a journey of *progress not perfection* and in this, we all need support. We hope this book is a companion to walk with you along the way. We begin this book with our own personal journeys, with the hope that they might inspire you to begin or continue yours.

It is such a privilege for us to be part of this incredible food revolution, as we all become more conscious of the impact food has on the planet and our health. We're so excited to have you join us, and we hope that you get inspired to 'Be a Plantier'.

Vivienne & Poornima

The Story of

PLANTIER

*I*t started with – of all things – basketball.

It was during those long hours of waiting for our sons to finish practice that we first started talking. And it was there, outside that sweaty gym in Copenhagen, Denmark, that we began to share our personal experiences and stories about food, health, and lifestyle choices. It didn't take long for us to realise that even though our paths had taken different twists and turns, the destination was the same: whole-heartedly embracing a plant-based diet and lifestyle.

And so the first seeds of Plantier were sown, born of a shared passion for a healthy, plant *and* planet friendly lifestyle, one which prioritised sustainability *and* filled with fresh, delicious and satisfying food.

Who We Are & Our Inspiration

*W*e love food, but over time we learnt that some food didn't love us back.

Over the years, sometimes with nothing more than a desire to feel better and alleviate the symptoms that were holding us back, we both adopted a plant-based lifestyle. What we discovered was that a plant-based diet was *exactly* what our bodies needed. We are living, breathing evidence of the huge difference this lifestyle choice has made in our lives, from more energy to better skin and gut health. But we weren't just looking inward; coupled with knowing the positive impact a plant-based diet has on the environment, we were more inspired than ever to create Plantier.

Part of our mission in founding Plantier was to inspire restaurants to provide a variety of menu options for people who choose to eat a plant-based meal, whether it's a lifestyle choice, a food intolerance or allergy or even just curiosity. Some of that stems from our own personal experiences – we were sick of going home hungry! We'd both experienced rumbling stomachs after a "meal" at a restaurant or a work function. We were more determined than ever in our desire to showcase just how delicious and satisfying plant-based meals can be.

Though we originally launched Plantier with a focus on catering and restaurants, it didn't take long to realise that there are many individuals who are plant-based curious, who are interested in finding out more about what 'going plant-based' actually means.

This was all the motivation we needed to mould Plantier into what it is today – a company with a social mission to *inspire individuals and restaurants to include a variety of delicious plant-based options on their menus.*

Since then, we both have graduated from the Plant-Based Nutrition Certificate Program from the Center for Nutrition Studies through eCornell, the online arm of Cornell University. Vivienne has also become a certified Integrative Nutrition Health Coach, through the Institute for Integrative Nutrition.

Who – or What – is a Plantier Anyway?

A shift in how we farm, how we eat, and how we think about food requires charting a new course forward. Sustainable, plant-based eating is, in many ways, a new frontier. In fact, the idea of a new landscape to be explored is one of the reasons we chose to name our enterprise Plant*ier*. A Plantier is a plant-based pioneer, exploring the possibilities of a rich, robust diet of plant-based, sustainable meals. A Plantier is someone who recognises the health benefits of a plant-based diet, but just as importantly, the environmental ones. In fact, the United Nations Sustainable Development Goals (SDGs) for 2030 were a major factor driving our vision.

Simply put, a Plantier is anyone, an individual or restaurant, who incorporates a variety of plant-based options. We are passionate in our belief that the future of sustainable food habits lies in incorporating more plant-based meals into our diet.

But what is a plant-based diet anyway? At Plantier, our definition of a *plant-based diet* is one that includes vegetables, fruits, grains, nuts, seeds and pulses from plant sources that are minimally processed, and that avoids all animal products including dairy, meat, fish and eggs. When possible, we also encourage using fresh, organic, seasonal produce.

At Plantier we work with individuals and those in the hospitality industry to encourage and inspire them to include a variety of delicious and substantial plant-based options on their menus, whether it's the weeknight family meal or the company canteen. We help our clients navigate this new frontier by breaking down the information surrounding plant-based food. We give them the tools they need to feel confident that adding more plant-based options at home and at restaurants is not just doable, but beneficial and profitable.

We want to guide, support, motivate and *inspire*. We want individuals to be able to choose delicious plant-based choices on every menu, everywhere, regardless of their food preferences.

Through our workshops, seminars and talks as well as coaching for individual consumers, chefs and restaurant owners, *we encourage individuals and restaurants to 'Be a Plantier' by including a variety of sustainable and delicious plant-based options on their menus* – for their own health and the health of our planet.

Vivienne's Journey...

As a child, I had cereal without milk, bread without butter, and during school lunchtime, was the only child without a carton of milk. I didn't like eggs and was picky about the meat I ate. Looking back, it's easy to see that my body was sending me clear signs, but at the time I was merely labeled a "fussy eater". During adolescence I switched to a "mostly" vegetarian diet, and ended up using dairy products, especially cheese, as a substitute for meat.

By the time I reached my mid-30s, I was exhausted. I was experiencing endless bouts of tonsillitis – and all the antibiotics to go with them – hives, fatigue, inflammation and a general lack of energy. I put it down to a busy lifestyle and chasing after two young children but in the back of my mind, it always felt like something wasn't 'quite' right. After reading stacks of books and numerous blogs about the impact of nutrition, I decided to embark on an elimination diet. After just 14 days, I was sold. I felt like a different person! Boundless energy, brighter eyes, smoother skin, and no inflammation were just a few of the benefits I was experiencing after just two weeks. Clearly, my childhood instincts were spot on, desperately trying to find ways to tell me what my body did and *didn't* need. Apart from my regret at not making the switch to a plant-based diet earlier, I haven't once looked back....and I haven't suffered a bout of tonsillitis since.

If you had suggested a plant-based diet to me years ago, the list of things that were "off-limits" would have terrified me. Yet with the explosion of inspirational food bloggers and cookbooks, not only am I no longer hesitant, I have discovered a true love of home cooking, experimenting and even hosting. Nothing makes me happier than when my meat-loving family and friends enjoy the plant-based meals I make.

This change in lifestyle is so much more than just what I eat. It has reignited the student within me, giving me the confidence to swap my marketing career for one that focuses on sharing the incredible healing benefits of a plant-based lifestyle. To my surprise, I've become a data geek, devouring all the research and evidence that supports the positive impact a plant-plentiful diet has on us as individuals and on our planet. It's my goal to bring those benefits into the mainstream, and to you.

Poornima's Journey...

My journey towards a plant-based diet and lifestyle likely began before I even became aware of it. Growing up in a vegetarian Indian family, I was familiar with a meatless diet, and in some ways that may have made my journey towards a plant-based lifestyle easier. My Mom is certainly the inspiration behind my own love for cooking healthy, nutritious food. I remember jumping off the school bus every afternoon excited to see what she had made for a snack or meal and relishing every bite. I spent hours in the kitchen with her, sometimes doing homework, other times helping out; all while my Mom dished out delicious food. I watched as she tried new recipes with enthusiasm, popping raw vegetables into her mouth as she cooked. She cooked meals from so many different cultures to this day I'm convinced that's why I grew up with a deep love for a variety of fresh, healthy food.

While this lifestyle at home was amazing, my Mom also tells me that I used to gag every time I had a glass of milk, often throwing up. I was a "scrawny" child, and my parents did what they thought was best; gave me more milk and dairy products, which they were taught would help me gain weight. Like so many others, I didn't know how to listen to the signals my body was sending me. And so I continued to suffer. Without adequate awareness and support in my early adulthood, I had to learn to manage food intolerances on my own through trial and error. I spent many years being my own laboratory, experimenting on myself, trying to figure out what caused the bloating and lack of energy that I had begun to assume was just a normal part of life I would have to live with. Then in 2010, a close friend of mine, Radhika, recommended that I read the book, *The China Study*.

The book changed my life. It led me to the decision to eliminate dairy and eggs from my diet and this made a huge, positive impact on my energy, health and general well-being. The conscious choice to transition to a plant-based diet wasn't easy, but what a difference it made! From energy, to skin, to general well-being, the benefits I experienced are too numerous to list.

While my plant-based journey may have started for health reasons, over time I became increasingly aware of the environmental impact of our food choices. Now one of the biggest drivers for me on my journey is the sustainability of our planet and our health. Through Plantier and the work we do, I hope to motivate more people to take ownership of their food choices for themselves and the planet we all share.

Cutting Through
THE CONFUSION

*W*hat comes to mind when you hear the term "vegan" or "vegetarian"? Did you conjure up images of tie-dyed tee-shirts and peace signs? Boring and bland foods and an endless list of all the things you'd miss out on? If so, we've got *great* news for you!

In truth, today's plant-based lifestyle choices bear almost no resemblance to the old stereotypes. From influential media and sports figures who have adopted a plant-based diet, to increased consumer choice, today's plant-based diet is not just limp salads and plates of raw vegetables. And as plant-based converts become more vocal, we're learning about more than just their food choices and habits, we're learning the reasons behind them as well.

Today, more than ever, we have better information about where our food comes from and the impact that our choices have on our health and on the environment. We are increasingly empowered to make conscious and conscientious decisions about what we eat, and what we don't.

Unlike restrictive diets or all or nothing trends, plant-based lifestyles are not just the next fad, they are here to stay. Global food consultants such as Baum and Whiteman predicted back in 2018 that plant-based eating isn't just the fashion, it's the future.[1] With the evidence mounting, it's hard to deny the many positive benefits of adopting a plant-rich diet, from tackling climate change to reduced risk of disease. As more and more people make the decision to adopt a plant-based lifestyle or even just incorporate more plant-based meals into their daily lives, the reasons for doing so increase as well. Here are just a few.

Food Intolerances

*F*ood intolerance, or food sensitivity, is our body's inability to digest certain food substances. In other words it's really not you, it's your food! Intolerances involve the digestive system and shouldn't be confused with food allergies, which affect the body's immune system. The most common food intolerances are dairy (milk and milk products, including cheese and butter), gluten, and caffeine, but there are plenty of other culprits. The symptoms of a food intolerance can begin fairly soon after eating the food, or can hide out in your system, only showing up a few days later, like a bad party guest. This can make identifying the source of your discomfort difficult. Common symptoms of food intolerances include bloating, fatigue, diarrhoea, abdominal pain, eczema, nausea and a runny nose. An elimination diet is one of the most effective ways to identify food intolerances. Speaking from experience, we found that one of the most valuable parts of the process is actually tuning in to how different foods make you feel.

Religious Dietary Requirements

While some people choose not to eat meat for personal reasons, others adhere to certain diet choices for religious reasons. Vegetarianism is traditionally practised among many religions throughout India including Hinduism, Jainism, Buddhism and Sikhism. Recent data shows that the percentage of vegetarians in India hovers between 20–38%. Numbers vary from state to state, but roughly speaking, that is nearly 500 million people, a substantial number who have chosen to adopt a meat-free diet.

Animal Welfare Protection

According to the WHO, annual meat production is projected to increase to 376 million tonnes by 2030, up from 218 million tonnes in 1997–1999.[2] Increasingly industrialised means of meat production to meet demand have resulted in conditions that many view as inhumane. There is a growing list of celebrities, like Joaquin Phoenix, Ariana Grande, Bryan Adams and Tobey Maguire, who have adopted a plant-based diet to protect the rights of animals. These very public figures are influencing others to follow suit. It's not just individuals either. Companies like abillion[3] are using their platform to raise awareness and funds for animal conservation efforts across the world.

Athletic Performance

What do Venus and Serena Williams, Lewis Hamilton, Jermain Defoe, and David Haye have in common? They are all top athletes in their fields who have adopted a plant-based diet. From cyclists to body builders, football players to Formula 1 drivers, tennis players to martial artists, the number of athletes who have touted positive performance benefits by adopting a plant-based diet is only growing. These athletes, like Hannah Teter, an American snowboarder and three-time Olympic medalist, are leading the way. In a 2017 interview Teter was open about the benefits of her plant-based diet: "I feel stronger than I've ever been, mentally, physically, and emotionally. My plant-based diet has opened up more doors to being an athlete. It's a whole other level that I'm elevating to. I stopped eating animals about a year ago, and it's a new life. I feel like a new person, a new athlete."[4]

The documentary *The Game Changers* shone a light on the positive impact of a plant-based diet on athletic performance, challenging age-old assumptions about the need for meat to build muscle and endurance.

Of course, the two biggest reasons for adopting a plant-based diet are probably the most important of all: our planet and our health.

Environmental Impact

Our food consumption habits and demands have a pretty hefty impact on the planet we all share. Later, we'll explore those impacts in a deeper way, but for now you should know that the three major ways in which animal agriculture negatively affects the environment are through greenhouse gas emissions, water consumption, and land usage and pollution.

Health

And finally, no conversation about a plant-based diet would be complete without listing the benefits to our health. Many consumers choose or are advised to cut down on meat for specific health reasons, such as lowering cholesterol or the risk of heart disease. If you're a burger aficionado who picked up this book out of curiosity, this next bit of information may be hard to swallow: There is strong evidence that shows the consumption of animal products can have a negative effect on our health, particularly when it comes to heart disease, cancer, dementia and diabetes. The great news is that making healthier choices has never been easier and you'll be joining an increasing number of people who are seeking healthier diets that are good for their bodies.

We've come a long way from our old ideas. We've expanded our understanding of how food choices affect us individually, and how they affect us environmentally. Each day we're increasing our awareness of how our choices affect more than just our waistline or our wallet.

But the truth is, we still have a long way to go.

And that's where we come in.

Are you ready to get nudged on your journey towards more sustainable and healthy food habits? If you're still not convinced, don't just take our word on it, here's what the experts think:

Transformation to healthy diets by 2050 will require substantial dietary shifts. Global consumption of fruits, vegetables, nuts and legumes will have to double, and consumption of foods such as red meat and sugar will have to be reduced by more than 50%. A diet rich in plant-based foods and with fewer animal source foods confers both improved health and environmental benefits."

- Prof. Walter Willett MD,
Harvard T.H. Chan School of Public Health[5]

Plantier's Nudges

 Make an Impact

 Cultivate Your Health

 Take Your Time

 Be Prepared

 Have Your Cake

Make
AN IMPACT

"The future of humanity and
indeed all life on Earth
depends on us."
- *Sir David Attenborough*

From Hunter-Gatherer to Aisle Browser

*U*ntil recently, most of the conversations around meatless diets focused on the source of our meat, or rather the *treatment* of that source. And whilst there is no denying cruelty to animals is still a major talking point, the discussion has expanded to include, if not focus on, the environmental impact of food production. But why is this such a hot topic anyway? Humans have been consuming meat for several million years, right?

The answer is more complex than a simple yes or no.

Over a relatively short period of time, our global consumption of meat has increased significantly. In fact, our consumption is almost double that of just 50 years ago. This meat and dairy heavy diet, adopted by the developed and developing world, has seen the average amount of meat consumed per person increase from 23kg in 1961 to 43kg in 2014.[6] At the same time, more than 820 million people still lack sufficient food.[7] With the population projected to grow by a further two to ten billion by 2050,[8] global meat consumption is only set to rise, as will food insecurity.

Unless there is a global food revolution.

The EAT-LANCET Commission was launched in 2019.[9] The commission is made up of 37 world-leading scientists from 16 countries across various scientific disciplines. The commission's goal is to reach a scientific consensus on how to feed the growing global population with a healthy diet that can be produced both efficiently and sustainably, using our existing planetary resources.

According to the EAT-LANCET Commission's summary report:[10]

"A radical transformation of the global food system is urgently needed. Without action, the world risks failing to meet the UN Sustainable Development Goals (SDGs) and the Paris Agreement, and today's children will inherit a planet that has been severely degraded and where much of the population will increasingly suffer from malnutrition and preventable disease."

What's the Link?

ut how much of a difference could eating a plant-based meal, reducing your meat-intake, or even being flexitarian or adopting a plant-based diet *really* have on climate change? How does the food we eat impact the environment?

Will it really make that much of a difference?

The short answer is a resounding yes.

Recent studies show that our food consumption, habits and demands do have a significant impact on the environment. Natural resources like land and water are finite, and our current usage is not sustainable. To continue feeding our growing population, we need change; one of those changes is to reduce or stop behaviours that contribute towards climate change.

Earlier we mentioned there were three primary ways that animal agriculture negatively affects the environment: greenhouse gas emissions; water consumption; and land usage and pollution. Let's dive right in.

The Greenhouse Gas Emissions of Food Production

reenhouse gases are gases, such as carbon dioxide, methane and water vapour. These gases absorb infrared radiation emitted from the Earth's surface and then re-radiate that radiation back. The greenhouse effect describes how these gases trap heat close to the surface, essentially acting as a greenhouse. Unlike a garden hothouse however, where a tomato plant might flourish, greenhouse gases are major contributors to the warming of our planet and to climate change.

In 2018, *Science* published the largest meta-analysis of global food systems to date. It showed that while meat and dairy provide us with just 18% of our calories and 37% of our protein, they produce 58% of agriculture's greenhouse gas emissions (GHG).[11] The global food system contributes between 10–30% of all greenhouse gas emissions.[12] In fact, animal agriculture features in the top four contributors to human made greenhouse gases alongside fossil fuels, transportation and manufacturing.[13]

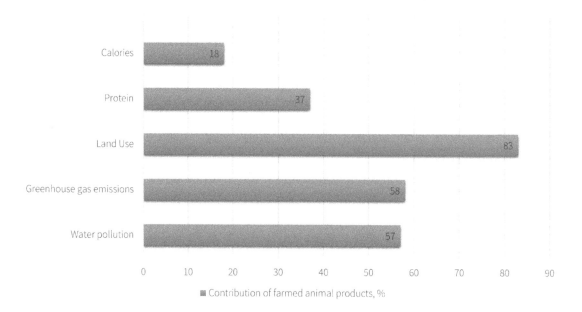

Environmental Impact vs Nutrition[14]

The next graph looks at the total GHG emissions per kilogram of 29 different food products - from beef to nuts. Using data from across more than 38,000 commercial farms in 119 countries, the researchers calculated the greenhouse gas emissions for a range of food products across the entire supply chain.[15] The research enables us to see at exactly which stage in the supply chain the food's greenhouse gas emissions originate. This extends from land use changes on the left, through to transport and packaging on the right.

While CO_2 is the most important GHG, it is not the only one – agriculture is a large source of methane and nitrous oxide as well. To capture all GHG emissions from food production, the researchers expressed them in kilograms of 'carbon dioxide equivalents'. For most foods - and particularly the largest emitters – most GHG emissions result from land use change, that is where human activity changes the natural landscape, such as deforestation (shown in green), and from processes at the farm stage (shown in brown). Farm-stage emissions include fertiliser use – both organic and synthetic; and enteric fermentation (the production of methane in the stomachs of cattle – colloquially known as "cow burps"). Combined, land use and farm-stage emissions account for more than 80% of the footprint for most foods. Given the information we usually hear about the impact of transportation of our food, it may come as a surprise to see that on the whole, it's a relatively small contributor to total emissions. For most food products, it accounts for less than 10%, and for the largest GHG emitters, it's much smaller; in beef from beef herds, for example, it's only 0.5%.

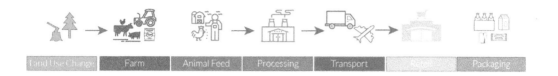

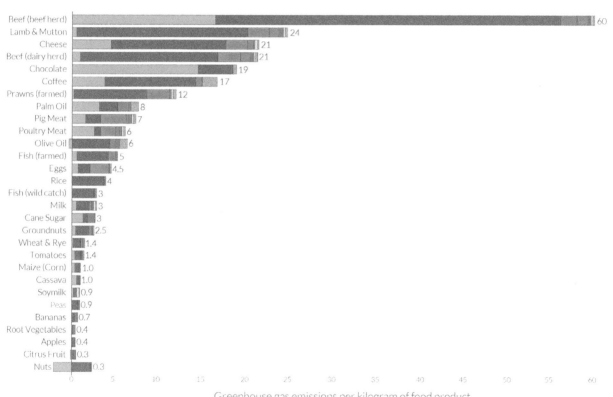

Greenhouse gas emissions per kilogram of food product
(kg CO$_2$-equivalents per kg product)

Greenhouse gas emissions across the supply chain[16]

For us, the most important insight from this study is that not all foods are created equally – at least when it comes to greenhouse gases. There are massive differences in the levels of greenhouse emissions for different foods. Overall, animal-based foods tend to have a higher footprint than plant-based. Producing one kilogram of beef emits 60 kilograms of greenhouse gases (CO_2-equivalents) vs. peas, which emit just 1 kilogram of gases per kilogram. Lamb and cheese both emit more than 20 kilograms of CO_2-equivalents per kilogram. Poultry and pork have lower footprints, but are still higher than most plant-based foods.

A good reason to give peas a chance, don't you think?

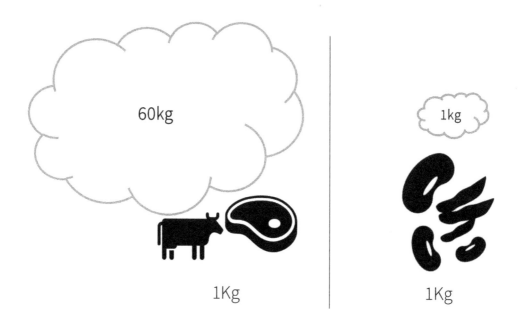

60kg

1kg

1Kg

1Kg

Yes, it is THAT different![17]

So how do the diets compare? Does a meat-eating diet contribute more GHG emissions? A study, conducted by the University of Oxford,[18] analysed the diets of thousands of meat eaters, vegetarians, fish eaters, and vegans. The study found that meat-rich diets resulted in 7.2kg of carbon dioxide emissions while both fish-eating and vegetarian diets produced about 3.8kg of CO_2 per day. A vegan diet? Only 2.9 kg.

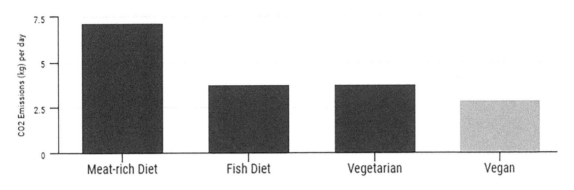

Comparison of emissions by diet type for a 2000kcal diet[19]

What about your milk choices?

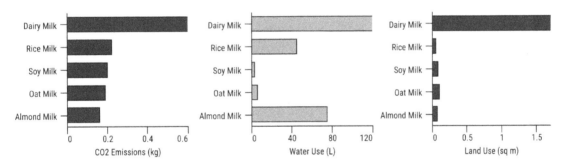

Environmental impact of 200ml of different milks[20]

Looking at the choices we make around milk also highlights that it's not solely GHG emissions we need to be concerned about. The *thirst levels* of our food, along with the land needed to produce them, point towards the need to develop a more holistic view of the environmental impact of the food we eat.

Vivienne & Poornima's Experience: Discovering our Gas-print

When we were doing the Plant-Based Nutrition Certificate Program from the Center for Nutrition Studies through eCornell, we spent a substantial amount of time learning about the environmental impact of various foods. Honestly, what we learnt shocked us. We then watched the Netflix documentary Cowspiracy and what we saw made us both question our own food habits – for ourselves and our families. The result was that we made conscious changes to the ingredients we bought and the frequency with which we consumed them. In our personal lives, our immediate family members are flexitarians and so consume some degree of eggs, meat and fish. We encouraged our families to watch Cowspiracy with us, which led us all to develop a much greater collective awareness of the environmental impact of our food choices. Change is not always easy, but as families, we made the decision to take a steady, gradual approach towards eating for a healthier planet.

Thirsty for More

The "thirst levels" of dairy and meat are significantly higher than fruits and vegetables and use about a third of the world's fresh water usage.[21] To give you a visual, *Cowspiracy* estimates that the fresh water needed to produce the meat in one hamburger is equivalent to an average person having two months of daily 4-minute showers.[22] So whilst we've all been diligent about turning the tap off when we brush our teeth, having shorter showers and using the low-flush button on the toilet, it turns out that popping to our local burger restaurant has a far greater impact on water consumption. Friends of the Earth[23] estimate that adopting a vegetarian diet (so still consuming some dairy products) could decrease your water-related footprint by 36%.

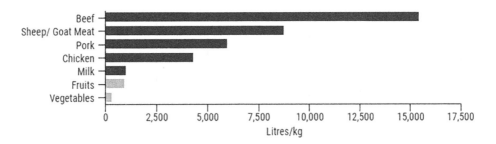

Thirst levels of food[24]

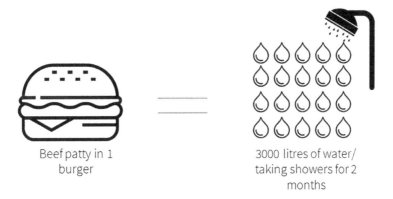

Beef patty in 1 burger = 3000 litres of water/ taking showers for 2 months

Can you believe this?[25]

Land of Not So Plenty

The statistics are stark: Livestock agriculture uses 80% of global land, yet produces less than 20% of the world's supply of calories.[26] According to the U.N. Convention to Combat Desertification,[27] it takes up to 10 pounds of grain to produce just 1 pound of meat, and in the United States alone, 56 million acres of land are used to grow feed for animals. In comparison, only 4 million acres are used to produce plants for humans to eat.[28]

The land needed to keep up with the growing global demand for animal products has grave consequences for our planet's forests as well. It is estimated that 1–2 acres of rainforest land are cleared every second,[29] and that animal agriculture is responsible for 80% of the current deforestation rates.[30] Deforestation and the burning of forests pollutes the environment and increases greenhouse gas emissions, further contributing to the greenhouse effect and warming of our planet. Industrial agriculture is responsible for 30% of deforestation in Africa and Asia, but close to an astonishing 70% in Latin America. Research published in 2021 reveals that because of the extensive deforestation of the Amazon rainforests, which rose nearly four-fold in 2019, the Brazilian Amazon released nearly 20% more carbon dioxide into the atmosphere over the past decade than it absorbed.[31]

The biggest drivers of deforestation include soy, palm oil, and cattle ranching. In fact soy, often associated with plant-based diets, is the second largest driver of deforestation after beef. But that only paints part of the picture: "only about 6% of soybeans grown worldwide are turned directly into food products for human consumption."[32] Also worth noting is that much of the soy we consume is organic, and grown primarily in North America, Europe and Asia.[33] What's alarming – from an environmental standpoint – is that the vast majority of the world's soy crop is produced for livestock feed using pesticide-laden, GMO monocultures in Central and South America.[34] With consumption of meat on the rise and more land needed for feed, this has led to further deforestation.

Naturalist Sir David Attenborough, in his acclaimed Netflix documentary *A Life on Our Planet*, provides sound advice:

When it comes to the land, we must radically reduce the area we use to farm so that we can make space for returning wilderness and the quickest and most effective way to do that is for us to change our diets...The planet can't support billions of large meat-eaters. There just isn't the space. If we all had a largely plant-based diet, we would need only half the land we use at the moment. And because we would then be dedicated to raising plants, we could increase the yield of this land substantially." [35]

It's not only our land that is in trouble, it's our water systems as well. Animal agriculture and crop production create pollutants which make their way into the Earth's water. These pollutants stimulate the growth of phytoplankton. These microscopic forms of algae eventually die, sinking to the sea bed, where they decompose. The process of decomposition consumes oxygen, which, in turn, creates "dead zones". These low-oxygen zones are inhospitable, killing off marine life or forcing them to migrate to other areas. Just how much damage can microscopic algae do? In truth, the impact of this nutrient water pollution is thought to be more devastating than the BP oil spill in 2010. And the problem is getting worse. According to a research study published in the journal *Science*, coastal dead zones have increased tenfold, while ocean dead zones have quadrupled since 1950.[36]

 Ever wondered how much of an impact your food choices have on the environment?

On the next page, we present the impact of some common food items. The data is based on the BBC's Climate Change Food Calculator.[37]

Food per serving	Annual green-house gas emissions (kg)	Water consumption in litres and number of showers lasting 8 minutes
½ avocado	15	3,519 L or 54 showers
150g of beans or just over ⅓ of a can	7	1,905 L or 29 showers
1 banana	5	714 L or 10 showers
75g beef/one typical fast food hamburger	604	3000 L or 60 showers*
1 handful of berries/grapes	9	2,618 L or 40 showers
1 slice of bread	4	1,928 Lor 29 showers
30g cheese, enough to cover two crackers	75	17,722 L or 272 showers
75g, or one small chicken breast	106	7,134 L or 109 showers
2 eggs	43	5, 381 L or 82 showers
140g, equivalent to one cod fillet (farmed)	146	39,646 L or 609 showers
1 glass of cow's milk (200ml)	49	9,800 L or 150 showers
1 glass of oat milk (200ml)	14	753 L and 11 showers
1 handful of nuts	1.1	10,426 L or 160 showers
3 tablespoons of uncooked rice	26	13,153 L or 202 showers
100g tofu	12	587 L or 9 showers

The data for the BBC Climate Change Food Calculator is based on the research conducted by the University of Oxford researchers Joseph Poore and Thomas Nemecek of the Agroecology and Environment Research Division in Zurich, Switzerland, who looked at the environmental impact of 40 major food products that represent the vast majority of what is eaten globally.

They assessed the effect of these foods on climate-warming greenhouse gas emissions and the amount of land and fresh water used across all stages of their production, including processing, packaging, and transportation, excluding the cooking process.

Poore and Nemecek analysed the data from nearly 40,000 farms, 1,600 processors, packaging types and retailers, to assess how different production practices and geographies have very different consequences on the planet. There will certainly be variations in the environmental impact of our food choices depending on where we live, accounting for transportation requirements and availability of fresh seasonal produce. Even so, the calculator serves as a powerful reminder of the impact of our food habits.

But What About the Avocado?

Whether you've already made the decision to eat sustainably or are just curious, it's likely you'll eventually encounter critics who may question your lifestyle food choices. Do they have a point? After all, there must be some variations in the production of plant-based food in terms of GHG emissions. What about avocados, mushrooms, cashews and cacao? A quick play around with the BBC's food calculator[38] shows that even the "greenest" of meat sources still produces more greenhouse gas emissions than plant-based proteins. It's important to know the facts. After all, knowledge is power!

* The water consumption for 75g of beef is an approximate taken from *Cowspiracy*'s data (https://www.cowspiracy.com/) as this information was unavailable through the BBC Climate Change Food Calculator at the time of print.

Did you know that each year, 11 billion avocados are consumed around the world?[39] **This is a result of the 'avocado boom'. Since the 1970s, this nutrient rich fruit has gained immense popularity and is sometimes even seen as a luxury good. It started as the must-have dinner party starter, the prawn and avocado cocktail, and has now gained almost cult-like status, with avocado toast a breakfast menu mainstay.**

The truth is, certain plant-based foods *do* have a much higher carbon and water footprint than others. It can take 60 gallons of water to produce a single avocado, whilst a kilogram of mangoes requires 150 gallons of water.[40] The carbon footprint of importing avocados to the UK results in a whopping 2.2kg of CO_2/kg for avocados[41] and 4.4kg of CO_2/kg for mangoes.[42] Data gathered from around the world, which took various aspects such as packaging and the amount of waste created during production and transport into account, puts the global carbon footprint of avocados at 0.55kg of CO_2/kg. For comparison, mangoes come out at 0.6kg of CO_2/kg. These figures may be even lower in reality because not all countries rely on transporting their fruit by air. Even if we take the highest numbers, the carbon footprint is still much smaller than beef and even the "greenest" farmed meat – chicken (4.1kg of CO_2/kg). The numbers around mushrooms vary. One study,[43] showed that producing a kilogram of the most common mushrooms, the kind we buy in the shops such as button, chestnut and portobello, emits 2.13–2.95kg of CO_2, while the US Mushroom Council says it is closer to 0.7kg.[44] Yet another study landed on a figure of 3 kg.[45]

What about cacao and cashews, do they deserve the bad press they often receive? The deforestation concerns of producing cacao are real. According to a report in 2017 by the World Bank,[46] 2–3 million hectares (4.9–7.4 million acres) of tropical forests were lost to cocoa plantations between 1988 and 2008. Whilst this is concerning, the crop only accounts for a tiny proportion of global forests cut down each year – palm oil and soy produced for livestock feed account for far more.[47] In terms of problematic plant-based crops, tree-nuts like cashews and almonds are the worst offenders – the villains of the environmental case for a plant-based diet. While the nutritional density of these nuts is very high, especially compared to rice and oats, their production requires significant water resources.

The dark side of food production, even for plant-based crops, goes beyond the devastating environmental impact. The investigative documentary series *Rotten* shone a new light on the secrets of avocado farming. With the soaring demand for avocados, the industry is lucrative; there's a lot of money to be made in avocado production. *Rotten* exposed the violence, which includes kidnapping, extortion, and even death, which has been linked to avocado production in Mexico and Chile. The series drives home the need for ethical consumerism: we need to buy fair trade products from farms and industries whose workers are guaranteed safe conditions and earning fair wages, all whilst protecting the environment.

It is, in the truest sense, food for thought.

In spite of all this, even the "worst" of plant-based foods imported from across the world are still better for the planet than livestock.

It's impossible to deny the impact our food preferences and demands have on our planet. That's the bad news. But there is good news: we still have time to rectify the damage we have done and prepare to sustain our growing population. The opportunity for us to live and eat sustainably, armed with the knowledge that our actions are saving the planet is there. We just have to grab it. Even more good news? With so many inspirational documentaries, chefs, cookbooks, apps and blogs, finding inspiration for plant-based meals has never been easier. Whether you're looking to go entirely meat-free or even just once or twice a week, now is the time.

...a dietary pattern higher in plant-based foods (for example vegetables, fruits, legumes, seeds, nuts and whole grains) and lower in animal-based foods (especially red meat) is both healthier and gives rise to lower greenhouse gas emissions and land-use change compared to existing diets."

- Global Biodiversity Outlook 5 (2020)[48]

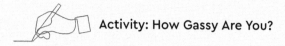 **Activity: How Gassy Are You?**

From the popular food items below, choose the 10 items that feature most frequently and in larger quantities in your diet by ticking the boxes. Write them in the table on the next page.

Next, visit the BBC's Climate Change Food Calculator at https://www.bbc.com/news/science-environment-46459714 or search the following in google to find the link: 'BBC climate change food calculator'.

Find out the annual greenhouse gas emissions for each of the 10 items. Add them up to get your annual carbon footprint of the top 10 food items in your diet.

☐ Apples	☐ Cheese	☐ Fish (farmed)	☐ Pork
☐ Avocados	☐ Chicken	☐ Lamb	☐ Potatoes
☐ Bananas	☐ Chocolate (dark)	☐ Milk (almond)	☐ Prawns (farmed)
☐ Beans	☐ Chocolate (milk)	☐ Milk (dairy)	☐ Rice
☐ Beef	☐ Citrus fruit	☐ Milk (oat)	☐ Tea
☐ Beer	☐ Coffee	☐ Pasta	☐ Tofu
☐ Berries & grapes	☐ Eggs	☐ Peas	☐ Tomatoes
☐ Bread			☐ Wine

10 items that feature in your diet most frequently and in larger quantities	How often do you consume them in a week?	Annual greenhouse gas emissions (kg)
	☐ 1–2 times a week ☐ 3–5 times a week ☐ Once a day ☐ Twice a day or more	
	☐ 1–2 times a week ☐ 3–5 times a week ☐ Once a day ☐ Twice a day or more	
	☐ 1–2 times a week ☐ 3–5 times a week ☐ Once a day ☐ Twice a day or more	
	☐ 1–2 times a week ☐ 3–5 times a week ☐ Once a day ☐ Twice a day or more	
	☐ 1–2 times a week ☐ 3–5 times a week ☐ Once a day ☐ Twice a day or more	
	☐ 1–2 times a week ☐ 3–5 times a week ☐ Once a day ☐ Twice a day or more	
	☐ 1–2 times a week ☐ 3–5 times a week ☐ Once a day ☐ Twice a day or more	
	☐ 1–2 times a week ☐ 3–5 times a week ☐ Once a day ☐ Twice a day or more	
	☐ 1–2 times a week ☐ 3–5 times a week ☐ Once a day ☐ Twice a day or more	
	☐ 1–2 times a week ☐ 3–5 times a week ☐ Once a day ☐ Twice a day or more	
	☐ 1–2 times a week ☐ 3–5 times a week ☐ Once a day ☐ Twice a day or more	

My annual carbon footprint (kg)
(Add the numbers in the last column to get this)

PLANTIER'S BIRCHER MUESLI

Serves 2 people; Nut free option

Imagine waking up in a wooden chalet high in the Alps greeted by fresh mountain air and the scent of cinnamon tickling your nose.
Plantier's Bircher Muesli is a quick, easy way to bring that mountain inspiration to your kitchen.

1. Mix together the oats, apple and plant milk in a bowl. Cover and let it soak overnight in the fridge.

2. Add the cinnamon and maple syrup. Mix through. Divide into two bowls.

3. Top with berries, nuts and seeds, as desired.

60g oats

1 apple, grated

150ml plant milk (we use oat milk; but you can use your favourite plant milk)

Sprinkle of cinnamon

Maple syrup, to taste (optional)

Handful of berries

6 almonds (optional)

Own choice of seeds e.g. chia, shelled hemp, sesame, pumpkin (optional)

MUSHROOM SOUP

Serves 4 people; Nut free

Nothing beats a hot bowl of soup when you're craving comfort and warmth, and this one could not be easier to whip up on a cold day. We love playing with the earthy flavours of different mushrooms and mixing and matching whatever spices we have on hand.

1. Put a pot on medium heat. Once hot, add the olive oil. Add the garlic and fry for half a minute until fragrant.

2. Add the mushrooms and give it a good stir. Add salt and cover for 3–4 minutes.

3. In the meantime, dissolve the organic vegetable stock cubes in the boiling water. Stir until completely dissolved. Add this stock to the mushrooms. Add the oat milk. Add pepper. Cover and simmer until mushrooms are fully cooked. This should take about 10–12 minutes.

4. If you have a glass jar blender, you can blend straight away. If not, wait for soup to cool before transferring the mushrooms and liquid into the blender. Blend well until smooth. Transfer back into the pot. Add the dried parsley. Give it a good stir and simmer for a further 5 minutes. If the soup is too thick for your liking, add a little water to adjust the consistency. Serve with warm bread.

1 tablespoon olive oil

4–5 cloves garlic, crushed or finely minced

800g button mushrooms (brown and/or white), sliced

2 cubes of organic vegetable stock

300ml boiling water

150ml unsweetened oat milk

1 teaspoon dried parsley (you could also use rosemary, basil or oregano depending on what you have in your spice jars)

Salt, to taste

Pepper, to taste

COUSCOUS SALAD
AND HARISSA TOFU

Serves 4 people; Nut free

We love this super flavourful and super quick weeknight meal. Parsley infused couscous pairs deliciously with harissa marinated tofu. The sweet, smoky flavour of the Tunisian chilli spice blend makes it an ideal partner for tofu!

Couscous salad

1. In a medium saucepan or large metal bowl, add the boiling water, olive oil and couscous. Stir, cover and let it rest for about 15 minutes until all the water has been absorbed and the couscous is dry. Gently fluff up the couscous with a fork to separate the grains.

2. In a large bowl, mix together the parsley, cucumber, cherry tomatoes, couscous and lemon juice. Add salt and pepper to taste.

3. Eat on its own or with the harissa tofu.

40g fresh curly-leaf parsley leaves, very finely chopped

265g cucumber or 1 cucumber, diced into small cubes

260g cherry tomatoes, quartered

300g (whole wheat) couscous

500ml boiling water

1 tablespoon olive oil

2 tablespoons lemon juice

Salt, to taste

Pepper, to taste

Harissa tofu

1. In a medium bowl, mix the harissa spice powder with the water to create a paste. Add the garlic, lemon juice and salt, stir well.

2. Add the tofu and mix well. Let it marinate for about 20 minutes to absorb the flavour.

3. Place a large frying pan on high heat. Once hot, add the oil and the tofu. Reduce to a medium heat and cook the tofu. Flip occasionally, taking care not to let the tofu break. Cook until the tofu turns medium brown and becomes slightly crisp on the outside.

4. Serve hot with the couscous.

550g firm tofu, cut into big cubes

2 tablespoons harissa spice powder* (adjust to your taste and preference)

4 tablespoons water

4 cloves garlic, crushed

Few drops of lemon juice

Salt, to taste

2 tablespoons oil

*Harissa spice powder is a spice mix found in many supermarkets, Middle Eastern/ African/Indian subcontinent food stores or online.

NUT CRUMB
AUBERGINE SLICES

Serves 4 people

Slightly crispy on the outside and soft on the inside, these slices are super versatile. We love them served with a dip as a starter or snack, but they are also a delicious addition to a lunch or evening bowl with veggies, rice or noodles.

1. Preheat the oven to 180°C (fan) and line two baking trays with parchment/baking paper.

2. Pour the oat milk into a shallow bowl.

3. Add all the dry ingredients in another shallow bowl, and mix thoroughly.

4. Using one hand, take one aubergine slice at a time and dip it into the oat milk. Turn it over to make sure that both sides and the edges have been covered. Shake it over the bowl to lose any excess milk.

5. Place into the bowl with the dry ingredients, and using the other hand, ensure that the whole slice is coated. Shake off any excess crumbs before placing on the baking tray.

6. Repeat until all slices are coated and then place the trays in the oven for 25 minutes or until they start to brown.

2 aubergines, cut into round slices about 1cm thick

50g almond flour/meal

1 tablespoon nutritional yeast

Pinch each of salt and pepper

½ teaspoon garlic powder

20g ground flaxseed

50ml oat milk

58

TACOS - 2 WAYS

Serves 4 people; Nut free

Who doesn't love taco night? The colours and flavours of traditional Mexican cuisine are all here. Pair one or both of our tacos – one with mushrooms and the other with pulled jackfruit – with a fresh, zesty salsa and creamy guacamole, and have a fiesta! Olé!

Mushrooms

1. Place a frying pan on medium heat. Once hot, add the olive oil. Fry the garlic on low to medium heat for about half a minute.

2. When the garlic is cooked slightly, add mushrooms, salt, pepper and chilli flakes. The mushrooms will release water so do not add any cooking liquid.

3. Cook the mushrooms until all the water has evaporated. The mixture should be dry.

1 tablespoon olive oil

5 cloves garlic, sliced

350g white and/or brown button mushrooms, washed, stems removed and sliced

Salt, to taste

Pepper, to taste

1 teaspoon chilli flakes

Jackfruit

1. Place a frying pan on medium heat. Once hot, add the olive oil. Fry the garlic on low to medium heat for about half a minute.

2. Add the jackfruit, taco seasoning, salt and about 50ml of water. Mix well. Add a little more water if needed, cooking until the jackfruit is cooked and the water has evaporated. This should take about 15 minutes. The mixture should be dry.

3. Once the jackfruit is soft, use a spatula and fork to separate it so it looks like pulled jackfruit. You can also use the back of the spatula to mash the jackfruit to get pulled jackfruit.

1 tablespoon olive oil

3 cloves garlic, crushed

1 medium red onion, sliced

2 × 400g cans of young/unripe jackfruit*, drained and rinsed

2 teaspoons store-bought taco seasoning

50ml water

Salt, to taste

Unfortunately, it's difficult to find young jackfruit in more sustainable packaging. We're hopeful this will change soon!

Salsa

1. Mix all the ingredients in a bowl. Adjust salt to taste.

5 big tomatoes, finely chopped

1 red onion, finely chopped

50g coriander leaves and stems, chopped

½ habanero chilli, very finely chopped (optional; you can also use any other green chilli that you find handy)

Juice of 1 lime

Salt, to taste

Guacamole

1. Add spring onions, coriander, green chilli and tomatoes and a little water (do not add too much) to a blender jar. Blend until coarsely mixed.

2. Cut the avocados in half. Remove the seed and scoop flesh out with a spoon.

3. Add the avocado, lime juice and salt to the blender jar. Blend again to the consistency desired. Some like their guacamole chunkier and others smoother. The choice is yours.

4 stalks spring onions or ½ red onion, chopped

30g coriander leaves and stems, chopped

½ large green chilli/1 small green chilli, finely chopped

1 tomato, chopped

4 small to medium sized avocados

Juice of ½ lime

Salt, to taste

Other Ingredients

10–12 tortillas
Coriander leaves to garnish
1 lime, cut into wedges

To assemble the tacos

1. Place a pancake/crepe pan on medium heat. Warm tortillas on the pan, following tortilla package instructions. Don't over-crisp the tortillas as that will cause them to break once folded in half.

2. Add either the mushroom or jackfruit filling.

3. Top with guacamole and salsa. Be generous!

4. Garnish with coriander leaves and squeeze a little lime.

EASY-PEASY YELLOW CURRY

Serves 4 people; Nut free

Confession: We love curry! This Thai-style curry is the perfect meal if you're craving the complex flavours of traditional curry but short on time. A real end of the workday treat.

1. Place a pot on medium heat. Once hot, add the oil and fry the onions and ginger on low to medium heat for about 3-4 minutes.

2. Add the red bell pepper and cook for about 5 minutes until it is soft, stirring occasionally. Add turmeric powder and chilli powder.

3. Add the coconut milk, vegetable stock, salt and water. Let it come to a boil on medium heat and then reduce heat to simmer for 5 minutes.

4. Add the sweet potato and cook until tender. Add salt to taste.

5. Add the chickpeas and baby spinach. Stir until spinach is wilted.

6. Serve with rice noodles or brown rice. Garnish with coriander leaves and spring onions.

1 teaspoon coconut oil

1 red onion, chopped

1 teaspoon ginger, peeled and grated

1 red bell pepper, chopped into 1cm pieces

1 ½ teaspoons turmeric powder

½ teaspoon chilli powder

2 medium sized sweet potatoes, peeled and cubed

75g baby spinach leaves, washed and drained

240g cooked chickpeas

800ml light coconut milk (or 400ml coconut milk and 400ml water)

2 teaspoons of vegetable stock powder or 1 cube of vegetable stock dissolved in 50 ml of warm water

200ml water

Salt to taste

Garnish with chopped coriander leaves and spring onions

JACKFRUIT BIRYANI

Serves 4–6 people; Nut free

Jackfruit is having a moment. The raw fruit has a hearty texture that makes it perfect to use in plant-based dishes like this Biryani, layered with flavour. Trust us, this one is worth the effort. Serve with natural, unsweetened coconut or soy yoghurt.

1. Put a large pot on medium heat. Once hot, add the oil. Fry the onions and garlic on low to medium heat for about 5 minutes, stirring occasionally, until the onions are soft.

2. Add the cumin seeds, cardamom pods, bay leaves, cinnamon stick, cloves and star anise. Stir for approximately 1 minute.

3. Add the tomatoes, turmeric and chilli powder. Stir on low to medium heat. Add a little water if needed to cook the tomatoes until they are soft, about 5–7 minutes.

4. Add the jackfruit and salt and give it a good stir. Let it cook for about 5 minutes.

5. Add the rice and water. Stir well, cover and bring to the boil on medium heat. Once the water begins to boil, reduce the heat to low and simmer until the water is fully absorbed and rice is cooked through. This should take approximately 20 minutes. Serve with natural (no added sugar) plant-based (coconut or soy) yoghurt.

1 tablespoon oil

2 medium-large red onions, sliced

4 cloves garlic, crushed

3 teaspoons cumin seeds

2 big black cardamom pods

4 bay leaves

½ cinnamon stick

6 cloves

2 star anise

3 tomatoes, chopped

1 teaspoon turmeric

¼ – ½ teaspoon chilli powder

3 × 400g cans of young/unripe jackfruit*, drained and rinsed (total drained weight: 675g)

4 teaspoons salt

485g basmati rice, rinsed and drained

700ml tap water

Unfortunately, it's difficult to find young jackfruit in more sustainable packaging. We're hopeful this will change soon!

Handy tip: Stir occasionally to avoid the rice at the bottom from burning. Depending on the rice used, you may need to add a little more water but add this water slowly in small quantities and add only what is needed. You want to ensure that the rice remains fluffy and separate, rather than mushy.

STIR FRY NOODLES

Serves 2 people; Nut free

What's better than a bowl of noodles? A healthy, colourful bowl of stir-fried noodles! We love the scent of ginger in a bit of sesame oil whilst we're making this one for our families. Who needs a takeaway when you can have a bowl of deliciousness on the table in under 20 minutes?

1. Mix rice vinegar, kecap manis and tamari in a bowl and keep aside.

2. Place a frying pan on medium heat. Once hot, add the sesame oil. Fry the onions and ginger on low to medium heat for about 5 minutes.

3. Once the onions have softened, add the tofu and fry for about 4–5 minutes until the tofu browns slightly.

4. Add bean sprouts and bok choy. Cook for 3–4 minutes but do not overcook the vegetables.

5. Add the cooked noodles, sauce mixture and toss well. Add salt and pepper if needed.

6. Serve garnished with spring onions.

1 teaspoon rice vinegar

2 tablespoons kecap manis (sweet soy sauce)*

3 tablespoons tamari/soy sauce

2 teaspoons sesame oil

1 medium red onion, sliced

1 teaspoon ginger, peeled and finely chopped

250g firm tofu sliced into strips

100g bean sprouts

4 stalks (about 240g) mini-bok choy, washed with bottoms cut off

200g whole wheat noodles, cooked as per package instructions

3 stalks spring onions, finely chopped

Salt, to taste

Pepper, to taste

You can substitute the kecap manis with a sauce made of 1 1/2 tablespoons of tamari/soy sauce and 1/2 teaspoon of maple syrup.

DRY CHILLI TOFU

Serves 4 people; Nut free

Tofu sometimes gets a bad rap, but the real beauty of tofu is that it takes on any flavour you give it. We love the flavours and colours of this dish, as well as its versatility. Serve with noodles or rice and voila! Lunch or dinner is served!

1. Place a large frying pan on medium heat. Once hot, add the sesame oil. Fry the onions and garlic on low to medium heat for about 5 minutes until onions are soft.

2. Add the whole dried red chillies and fry for a minute.

3. Add the kecap manis, rice vinegar and tamari. Stir and add the tofu. Adjust salt to taste.

4. Serve with noodles or rice, and our stir-fry broccoli/broccolini.

1 tablespoon sesame oil

1 medium red onion, sliced

3 cloves garlic, thinly sliced

4–6 whole dried red chillies

4 teaspoon kecap manis (sweet soy sauce)*

½ teaspoon rice vinegar

1 tablespoon tamari/soy sauce

550g firm tofu, drained and cut into big rectangular pieces

Salt, to taste

> You can substitute 2 tablespoon kecap manis with a sauce made of 1 ½ tablespoon of tamari/soy sauce and ½ teaspoon of maple syrup.

PAV BHAJI
(VEGETABLE CURRY
WITH BREAD)

Serves 4 people; Nut free

*Full of flavour from traditional spices, this popular
Indian street food dish definitely packs a plantiful punch.*

1. Place the potatoes, carrots, green peas and green pepper in a large pot with plenty of water on medium to high heat, and boil until the vegetables are tender. Reserve about 100ml of the cooking water for later. Drain the vegetables and set aside. (You can keep the drained water as a base for a soup).

2. Place a pot on medium heat. Once hot, add the oil and fry the onions, ginger and green chillies on low to medium heat for about 8 minutes until the onions are browned. This browning of the onions is where much of the flavour of the dish comes from, so be patient as you do this.

3. Add the tomatoes and the pav bhaji masala. Fry well. Add some of the reserved cooking water and let it cook until the tomatoes are soft and well cooked, about 5 minutes.

550g potatoes, peeled and diced into 1cm cubes
250g carrots, peeled and diced into 1cm cubes
150g frozen green peas
1 green pepper, core removed and chopped
2 tablespoons oil
2 medium-large red onions, chopped
1 tablespoon piece ginger, peeled and grated
½ green chilli, deseeded and very finely chopped (optional)
3 tomatoes, chopped
2–3 teaspoons Pav Bhaji masala* (depending on your comfort with spice)

4. At the same time, mix the onions and chopped coriander leaves and stem for the garnish and set aside.

5. Add the drained vegetables, salt and about 100ml of the reserved water. Cook on medium heat until the water evaporates and vegetables are very soft. This should take about 10 minutes. Then mash the vegetables well with a potato masher.

6. Top with the onion-coriander mixture and a squeeze of lime. Serve with toasted whole wheat rolls or burger buns.

Salt, to taste

4–6 whole wheat bread rolls or burger buns, sliced in half

Garnish:
1 medium red onion, finely chopped
50g coriander leaves and stems, finely chopped
1 lime, cut into wedges

* Pav Bhaji masala is a spice mix found in Indian or online stores.

Cultivate

YOUR HEALTH

"Let food be thy medicine and medicine be thy food."
- *Hippocrates*

*B*efore we really dive in, we want to stress that our approach is not a 'diet', not in the restrictive sense that many of us are used to. Instead, it's to inspire you to look for ways to add more plant-based foods into your everyday meals. There will be foods that you like, and some that you don't; some will fill you with energy, others may not. Your journey is yours, and yours alone. Although we are both totally plant-based, we each have different foods that don't agree with us. We encourage you to enjoy experimenting and finding what works best for *you*.

One of the most empowering and encouraging messages we have taken from our studies is this: our health is in our hands. What an incredible message, and one which is especially important to remember whenever we feel as if we are bombarded with statistics about the rapid deterioration of our collective global health.

If we pull back and look at the bigger picture, the scene looks grim. In 2021, the World Health Organization (WHO) reported that noncommunicable diseases account for 71% of global deaths annually.[49] Of these, 80% are from four groups: cardiovascular diseases, cancers, respiratory diseases and diabetes.

The good news is that we can do something about it: our health is in our hands. By taking a preventative rather than curative approach, together we could reduce the risk of developing these diseases by up to 80%![50] The remedy isn't complex. It doesn't require years of research or billions in funding. So what's the magic answer? Lifestyle. Put simply, the way we are living, moving and eating determines much of our health. While there are factors that are outside of our control, like genetics or environment, we have far more power than we are led to believe.

One of the lifestyle changes the WHO identified in their report is the importance of following a healthy diet. Other lifestyle factors to be aware of include tobacco use, physical inactivity and the harmful use of alcohol, but it's the emphasis of a healthy diet that we will focus on in this section.

When Did Food Stop "Being Thy Medicine"?

*M*ore than 2,000 years ago, the famed Greek physician Hippocrates is credited with advising his patients to *"let food be thy medicine"*. With all the knowledge, research, and technological advances we have made over the last two millennia, how did we lose sight of what should be common sense advice? What went wrong?

Following World War II, there were significant changes to our food system, everything from how our food was produced, to how and where it was consumed. The rapid development of synthetic chemicals enabled crops to grow bigger, faster and stronger, with significantly improved yields. Shelf-lives grew longer, which meant crops could be shipped around the world to more markets. Those same chemicals have changed the colour, texture and flavour of our food to increase their desirability. But at what cost?

Chemicals have made their way not only into our medicine cabinets, but also into the food and drink we're consuming everyday. In the UK, 26% of all the antibiotics administered are given to farm animals.[51] In the US, though usage has reduced since its peak in 2015,[52] it's estimated that 50% of chickens are still routinely given antibiotics.[53] As a result, the meat and dairy products we are buying and consuming are contributing to antibiotic resistance, something that the World Health Organization has identified as one of the biggest threats to global health and food security.[54]

Go With Your Gut

*T*he gut has always been considered an integral part of the digestive system, but there is increasing evidence that our guts play a significant role in our *overall* health and well-being. Processes in the gut impact our whole body, and research links gut health to everything from blemishes and signs of ageing, to anxiety and depression, as well as diseases such as diabetes and obesity.[55]

Did you know that the gut:

- Represents about 70% of the entire immune system?[56]
- Manufactures approximately 95% of the body's serotonin, often called the happy hormone?[57]
- Produces about 50% of dopamine, which is associated with our feelings of pleasure?[58]

2,000 years later and we are still learning about the wonders of the human body. Take our gut microbiome, which is made up of about 100 trillion bacteria, fungi and parasites, and approximately 500 trillion mini-viruses. Like our DNA, our gut microbiome is unique to each and every one of us.[59] What we put in our gut has a direct and profound impact on a wide range of functions in our bodies.

Following decades of focus on eating for our weight and our waistlines, it feels like we are in the midst of a paradigm shift. Rather than just eating to achieve a magic number on the weighing scales, the attention is now on eating for our health, in the present and in the future. As leading Neurologists Drs. Ayesha and Dean Sherzai say, every meal has the potential to *"heal us or harm us"*.[60] The Sherzais and other pioneering doctors are encouraging this shift in focus, from eating only in regard to our weight, to eating for the health of our whole body, addressing not only the things we can see, but also everything we can't.

Here's something to chew on:

Did you know that the human brain accounts for 2% of the body's weight but it consumes up to 25% of the body's energy?[61]
So we need to make sure we feed it well!

Make Your Rainforest Thrive

The gut microbiome is frequently likened to a rainforest, an environment that thrives on diversity and lives in delicate balance. And just as we're seeing the destruction of rainforests on Earth, some believe that we are unknowingly experiencing a deforestation of our gut microbiome. Our lifestyles are filling us with chemicals – highly processed foods, household cleaning products, regular use of medication, chronic stress – affecting the balance of our gut ecosystem. Whilst stopping the deforestation of the world's tropics and forests might feel like it is out of our personal control, helping the rainforest in our bodies flourish is absolutely in our hands. Or more accurately, in our guts.

As gastroenterologist Dr Will Bulsiewicz says: "Food is the #1 determinant of health and disease in your lifetime".[62] Increasing numbers of doctors, researchers and health professionals all agree that we need to understand the impact of our food choices on our health. They also agree that the route to a healthy mind and body is a plant-rich diet obtained from a diverse range of fruits, vegetables, grains, nuts, seeds, pulses, herbs and spices.

In addition to the food choices we make, there are many other things we can do to help foster thriving and healthy diversity in our gut:

- Find techniques to reduce and manage our stress levels naturally, through activities like deep breathing, yoga and meditation.

- Swap harsh cleaning products for homemade versions or brands that use plant-based and biodegradable ingredients (many of these products are packaged in recycled bottles, helping you reduce your plastic consumption at the same time as cleaning up your home).

- Spend time in nature; walking, running, swimming and gardening, no matter your natural surroundings just breathe in that fresh air.

Vivienne's Experience: Listen to Your Gut

*Inflammation is a vital bodily function. It helps us heal when we have bumps and grazes and helps us figure out when our body is out of balance. But there is another potentially more harmful type of inflammation. **Low-level inflammation** is chronic, system-wide inflammation that occurs when our bodies are in an almost constant state of repair.*

My inflammation was particularly noticeable and pronounced in the morning. I'd wake up and feel the stiffness in the joints of my knuckles. As I got out of bed, I'd feel the ache in my back and shoulders. If it was particularly bad, I'd feel it in my feet. A puffy face would stare back at me from the mirror, my features exaggerated. My eyes seemed to suffer the most. Throughout the day my symptoms would ease and I would forget about them until it happened again.

My bouts of inflammation would come and go. To be honest, I didn't think much of it until I read an article written by Dr. Nigma Talib. Every word connected with my experience. It was like she was writing about me. I purchased her book, Reverse the Signs of Ageing: The Revolutionary Inside-Out Plan to Glowing, Youthful Skin, which sounded like an odd title given the topic of the article, but equally I wasn't going to turn down the opportunity for younger looking skin!

I devoured the book on holiday and immediately booked an appointment with a nutritionist for when we got home. What I read was both eye-opening and empowering. It was a turning point for me. I stopped eating to lose or maintain weight and started eating to heal and energise my body. Most importantly though, it made me realise that the gut was the starting point of this healing process.

Horn of Plenty

Welcome to our "kitchen", a place where food is not only delicious, it nourishes your body and your mind. This is where we'll give you the knowledge and the confidence to take control of your health and well-being. We'll offer you a practical guide to help you put more health-promoting plant foods onto your plate, in a way that works for *you*.

Even though the foods we outline below are all nutrient-packed, they may not all work for you. Try to tune in to how foods make you feel, both immediately and some time after eating them. Do they make you feel good? Do they give you energy and concentration so you don't feel like reaching for a snack soon after a meal? Or do they make you feel not so good; bloated and/or gassy, bursts of energy followed by a slump, or a lack of concentration? Also, be aware of your mood. Do you feel happy or angry, positive or negative, calm or tense? What we eat can greatly impact how we feel, both physically and emotionally. It can take time and patience to tune in to your body this way, and keeping a food diary is a great tool to help you do just that.

To create your own food diary, turn to page 279, where you will find a food diary template, along with some guidance on how to use it.

Free From Labels, Not Free-From Labels

Traditionally, a vegan diet was what we would now recognise and describe as a whole-food, plant-based diet. That plant-plentiful diet, rich in nutrients, is the one which we focus on in this book. However, just because the label reads "vegan" doesn't mean all foods are created equal. With the rise in popularity of a vegan diet, food companies have jumped on the commercial bandwagon. The result is sometimes highly processed foods that twist the idea of "healthy". Be careful, foods labelled 'vegan' or 'plant-based' aren't automatically "good for you". Check the ingredients label. If it's lengthy, and loaded with ingredients you can't visualise, approach them in the same way as you would any other processed food, with caution and eat occasionally. Products that feature health claims on the label are often trying to hide the bad stuff, typically extra or highly processed sugar and salt. As much and as often as possible, we encourage you to use foods in their original, unprocessed form. A few tips:

- Keep it real, keep it whole (more on that later!)
- Buy foods that are free from labels, not packaged in 'free-from' labels. They are better for you, and better for the planet!

Supplements, taken under the guidance of a qualified practitioner or through choice, is a personal decision. We encourage you to eat your vitamins wherever possible, rather than get them from pills, as we believe that there is no amount of supplements that will compensate for an unhealthy lifestyle.

Balance Your Plate

One component to keeping it real and keeping it whole, as well as making delicious, satisfying meals that provide your body and mind with all they need, is learning to balance your plate. Though it sounds a bit like a circus trick, it involves not just balancing the right mix of carbohydrates, protein and vegetables, but enhancing these with texture and flavour. The key to a balanced plate is variety, not just at each meal time, but every day and every week. Keep it fresh and interesting by mixing it up as often as you can.

We know it can be intimidating or difficult to try something new, which is why we've included a visual guide to help you on your way towards creating a healthy, filling and tasty balanced plate (or bowl!) for every mealtime. Use this as a sense check to make sure that you're covering all bases, and whether or not you need to add a dash of something extra.

Protein

25% of plant protein:
legumes, lentils, nuts, seeds,
tofu, chickpeas

Vegetables

50% of vegetables from the
abundant and seasonal
options available

Carbohydrates

25% of carbohydrates:
quinoa, millet, rice, sweet
potatoes, amaranth

Texture & Flavour

The dish should contain
texture and flavour with the
use of herbs, spices, and
mushrooms and their stock
for flavour enhancement.

Start Counting Plants, Not Calories

If you've ever struggled with your weight, you're no doubt familiar with the calories in vs. calories out equation. In reality, it isn't that straightforward. Quite simply, all calories are not created equal.

When we look at the ingredients list on the packaging, calories only provide us with a snapshot of a food, not the whole picture. It's time to start thinking less about the calories and more about how the foods are going to benefit you and how they will make your mind and body feel. The gut feeds off what we put in it. It craves plants because plants provide us with vital nutrients and fibre. The gut also craves diversity. Researchers from the world's largest published study to date on the gut microbiome (including The American Gut Project and British Gut) have discovered that we should be aiming for at least 30 different plant-based foods a week.[63] So rather than counting calories, try counting the number of plant-foods you're eating every week. Your gut and brain will thank you.

Vivienne's Experience: The Sugar Rollercoaster

As a teenager, there were times when I limited myself to a mere 1000 calories a day, whilst also playing a lot of sport. My focus was always to lose weight, not to get healthy. I tried to 'cheat' the system with low calorie foods, not considering that they were highly processed and full of sugar (or chemical alternatives!). Far from cheating the system, I was just cheating my body. I was often hungry, craving more sweet foods and just generally obsessing over what and when I would next eat.

When we eat highly processed, sugary foods, our blood sugar spikes and then drops, leaving us feeling hungry and unsatisfied. We reach for another low-calorie food and the same thing happens, our blood sugar spikes and we're quickly left feeling hungry, again. And so the cycle repeats, until we decide enough is enough and quit the calorie counting. Not because we lack will power, but because we're hungry!

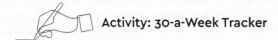 **Activity: 30-a-Week Tracker**

The American Gut Project has identified that we need a minimum of 30 different plant foods a week to help keep our gut healthy. Over the course of 7 days, keep a track of every type of plant food you eat by writing it in the 'food' column and then putting an 'x' to indicate the food group it sits under. Only count each food **once** over the course of the week. For example, if you have oats for breakfast several times and oat milk in your coffee everyday, only list oats one time. Remember, it is the variety of the different food groups that you are looking for. As you keep a record, you can start to spot opportunities to bring diversity to different food groups.

If you're not sure which category your food falls into, the rest of this section should help to clarify. If you aren't sure about how much of these foods to eat, you might like to take a look at your country's nutritional guidelines for guidance on their recommended portion sizes.

Food	Fruit	Vegetables	Grains	Pulses	Nuts/ Seeds	Herbs/ Spices
1.						
2.						
3.						
4.						
5.						
6.						
7.						
8.						
9.						
10.						
11.						

12.						
13.						
14.						
15.						
16.						
17.						
18.						
19.						
20.						
21.						
22.						
23.						
24.						
25.						
26.						
27.						
28.						
29.						
30.						

Poornima's Experience: Enough is Enough

Am I getting enough variety? This was a question that had been bothering me. It's so easy with our busy lives to stick to using the ingredients we are most familiar with and cooking dishes we are most comfortable rustling up. So I was concerned about not having the kind of plant variety needed to reap the benefits of a healthy gut. I was sharing this with Vivienne on one of our many weekly calls, and before we'd stopped speaking, she had already sent me the 30-a-week tracker she'd been using with her clients. This was such a great way to know and reassure myself that I was indeed on the right track, while also providing motivation for areas to do better in. After all, there's always room for more progress!

Paint Your Plate

An array of colours on our plate doesn't just make it look more enticing, it also means that we're getting a wealth of goodness. The richer the colour of the food, the more polyphenols it contains. Polyphenols are the micronutrients we get from plants. They include both vitamins and minerals and play a fundamental role in our everyday functioning, with each one offering different benefits to our health and well-being. Painting your plate with colour means giving your body what it needs, really making sure it and you are getting the valuable combination of micronutrients. Learning the science of micronutrients can feel like you're learning the periodic table of food, so we've outlined a few of the vitamins and minerals typically found in food colour groups.

Whilst there are differences between the colours, there are number of benefits they all have in common:

- High in fibre. Fibre helps us to feel full for longer, regulates blood sugar and aids digestion. It has also been linked to a reduced risk of heart disease, type 2 diabetes, stroke and bowel cancer.[64]

- High water content. As well as keeping well-hydrated by drinking plenty of water, the high water content of these foods offers a way to eat your water too.

- Anti-inflammatory properties. By eating these in abundance, and in wide variety, we help to reduce the risks of inflammation and the many diseases associated with it.

More Than a Side Dish

Fruits and vegetables shouldn't be confined to acting as an accompaniment to your evening meal, try to give them centre-stage in all your meals throughout the day. Guidelines on how much fruit and vegetables you should consume vary from country to country, but research has shown that very few people actually reach the recommended daily quantities. In the UK, all age and gender groups eat less than the recommended five-a-day, and in the US, only one-in-ten American adults consume the four to five cups a day advised in the federal guidelines.[65] With so many varieties to choose from, why not look to buy a different one the next time you go shopping, or challenge yourself to try a recipe using an unfamiliar fruit or vegetable? There are so many recipes available online, you're bound to find one that you love!

The Rainbow of Fruits and Vegetables

Red

Main vitamins and minerals – folate, potassium, vitamins A, C, and K1.
What should I eat? Strawberries, raspberries, cherries, red grapes, red grapefruit, cranberries, watermelon, apples, pomegranate, tomatoes, beetroot, red bell peppers, red onion.

Orange and yellow

Main vitamins and minerals – folate, potassium, vitamins A and C.
What should I eat? Bananas, pineapple, cantaloupe melon, peaches, sweetcorn, yellow peppers, mango, oranges, tangerines, apricots, carrots, sweet potatoes, pumpkin, butternut squash.

Green

Main vitamins and minerals – folate, magnesium, potassium, vitamins A and K1.
What should I eat? Kiwi fruit, apples, pears, green grapes, avocado, asparagus, spinach, broccoli, kale, cabbage, brussel sprouts, rocket/arugula, courgette/zucchini, edamame, peas, mange tout, swiss chard, lettuce, artichoke, jackfruit, and green herbs like basil, mint, rosemary, sage and thyme.

Blue and purple

Main vitamins and minerals – manganese, potassium, vitamins B6, C and K1.
What should I eat? Blueberries, blackberries, dark grapes, plums, figs, raisins, prunes, aubergine/eggplant, purple cabbage.

White and brown

Main vitamins and minerals – folate, magnesium, manganese, potassium, vitamins B6 and K1.
What should I eat? Onions, garlic, leeks, mushrooms, white potatoes, parsnips, cauliflower.

The Rainbow of Fruits and Vegetables

How to Paint Your Plate
A simple approach to ensure you're getting enough everyday is by aiming to have:
At least two portions at every meal time.

Breakfast ideas:

- Stir in a grated apple to overnight oats.
- Top overnight oats, porridge, chia pudding or coconut yoghurt with chopped fresh fruit.
- Make a simple, no added sugar compote by cooking a bag of frozen berries in a pan until the juice starts to turn into a syrup.
- Make a smoothie or smoothie bowl with a combination of fruits and vegetables.
- Top wholemeal or rye bread with avocado or mushrooms.

Lunch and dinner ideas:

- Add chopped pepper, cucumber or grated carrots to sandwiches and wraps.
- Have a soup recipe for every colour of the rainbow and try to add at least two different vegetables (adding onion and garlic to every recipe brings more goodness and flavour too!).
- Create a power bowl with your favourite whole grain, several veggies (cold or cooked), nuts, seeds and a dip made from pulses.
- Add some extra vegetables like sweetcorn, peppers or sweet potato to a pot of chilli.
- For a lighter option, use vegetables instead of grains, for example, courgetti, cauli rice and sweet potato noodles.
- Jackfruit, because of its 'pulled' texture, is a natural alternative to meats like pork and chicken. Use it in tacos, curries, tagines, spring rolls. Don't be shy adding some spice!

One with every snack – this may be one or two a day, and if you don't worry, just add an extra variety into your meals.

Snacks

- Use fruit instead of sugar to sweeten up homemade oaty bars or flapjacks. Ripe bananas or soaked dried fruit provide the perfect combination of sweet and sticky.

- Core an apple, slice it into rings and top with your favourite nut or seed butter.

- Blitz up a smoothie with a combination of fruits, or fruits and vegetables.

- Cool down with some banana ice cream, by blitzing a couple of pre- frozen bananas. You might like to add some of your favourite plant milk to make blending a little easier and the ice cream a little smoother.

- Chop up some peppers, cucumber, carrot and celery sticks to go with your favourite bean dip.

Organic and Seasonal

Vivienne's Experience: Chocolate Confusion

I used to work for a confectionery company and helped launch their first box of organic chocolates. As the handling processes were so different in the factory, I needed to brief the team that would be packing them so they understood the tight regulations involved in achieving organic status. When asking the team if they had any questions, the first one I was asked was not about regulations, but why the company was going to sell a 'healthy' range of chocolates in the first place, when the confectioner was known for indulgent treats. It took me a while to convince them that the only healthier aspect of organic chocolate is the way it is grown and processed. The proof that organic and indulgent could co-exist came when we tasted them!

That was about 15 years ago and whilst organic has become more mainstream since then, it's probably useful to start with a definition.

The EU definition of organic farming/production[66] means a sustainable agricultural system respecting the environment and animal welfare, but also includes all other stages of the food supply chain.

The key principles include:
- The use of chemical pesticides and synthetic fertilisers is banned.
- Antibiotics are severely restricted.
- GMOs are not allowed.
- Crops are rotated.

The amount of organic produce available varies depending on where you live and whether it's been prioritised by the government, local producers and sellers. It is also typically more expensive than mass-produced food.[67] The increased cost is because organic produce is more labour-intensive to produce and process, yields are lower and, at least at the moment, demand is lower so economies of scale haven't yet been achieved. There are also costs that support the ongoing welfare of the environment, farmers and their employees. When you're trying to manage your weekly food shopping spend, especially those of us who must stick to a budget, buying organic food doesn't always feel like a priority.

You want to make sure you're getting the biggest bang for your organic buck, but how do you know where your money is best spent?

One useful tip we came across is prioritising those foods that you would rinse and eat, versus those that can be shelled or peeled.

Several countries produce a *dirty dozen* list to identify the foods found to have the highest level of pesticide residue. The testing is not without fault but it provides some guidance when it comes to choosing which products to prioritise buying organic. In the UK, Pesticide Action Network UK (PAN-UK)[68] produces a list and in the United States, it is the Environmental Working Group (EWG).[69] After analysing UK government data from 2018 and 2019, PAN-UK have identified the most recent *dirty dozen*[70] to be:

- Grapefruit
- Clementines, Mandarins and Satsumas
- Strawberries
- Pre-packed salad
- Grapes
- Lemons
- Peaches and Nectarines
- Pears
- Spinach
- Chilli Peppers
- Apples
- Blackberries and Blueberries.

In addition, it helps to know the hands that feed you. When you buy locally grown, seasonal produce, it offers benefits to both you and the wider community:

- Supports local growers. If your area has regular farmer's markets, it gives you the opportunity to ask questions about their growing practices. Ask questions like: What sprays or pesticides do you use? What variety of crops do you grow? They may even be open to you visiting their farm.

- Helps you eat in season. Eating as nature intended often gives a fuller flavour, richer colour and more nutrients. Summer strawberries are the perfect example. Have you ever been tempted to buy strawberries as soon as you see them on the shelves? The tip of the fruit can be beautifully red but there's still a thick white layer peeping out from under the leaves. This is nature's way of telling us to be more patient.

● Reduces the impact of food transportation both on the environment and the quality of the food. Without the travel time, the produce will have been picked when it's ready, and will be fresher for not having been transferred from one mode of transport to another.

If there's a fruit or vegetable that you love to eat all year round, it might be worth checking the freezer aisles. When fruits and vegetables are frozen whilst fresh they retain their nutrients. They can often be a cheaper option than buying fresh, and are a great way to reduce food waste, by only using what you need.

Grains – Keep it Real, Keep it Whole

Trust us, we've felt overwhelmed staring at the array of grains available. With different shapes, sizes, colours and processing methods, it can be hard to know which to choose. Do I want bulgur or barley? Quinoa or couscous? As a general rule of thumb, always go for the whole grain option!

Whole grains are high in fibre, which means the body digests them more slowly, which means we feel fuller for longer and maintain stable blood sugar levels. Eating a diet rich in fibre supports the digestive process and aids in the prevention of constipation. And if you're considering plant-based options and worried about iron, whole grains are a great source.

 If you experience constipation, you're not alone. It is estimated that 12% of the world's population struggle with this condition.[71]

Most adults in the UK are eating about 18g of fibre a day, a whopping 12g short of the recommended daily intake of 30g.[72] A natural way to try and relieve the problem, is to eat a plant/fibre rich diet of whole grains, vegetables, fruits and pulses, as well as keeping well-hydrated.

Look for '100% whole grain' to make sure it has not been mixed with refined versions. Refined grains, like white flours, breads, pastas and rice don't boast the same nutritional qualities as whole grains.[73] Refined grains are processed, usually to extend their shelf-life and give them a finer texture, but in the processing the most nutritious parts of the grain – the bran and the germ and thereby the fibre – are removed. Unlike the fibre-rich whole grain versions, refined grains spike your blood sugar and leave you feeling hungry more quickly. Because of their long shelf-life, they're commonly used in combination with sugars to make highly processed foods like cakes, biscuits, pastries and cereals. These doubly processed foods have an even more exaggerated impact on your blood sugar. A diet of predominantly highly processed foods can send us on a blood sugar roller coaster that leaves us feeling hangry. When you see media headlines giving carbohydrates a hard time, it's often because an abundance of these highly processed options have given their whole grain counterpart a bad name.

How to Make it Whole

Here are some simple ways to swap and switch out your grains to increase your fibre intake and steady your blood sugar levels.

Oats

Even the healthiest sounding breakfast cereals can be laden with sugar. The cereals with a sole ingredient in their title may *sound* like they are made of healthy components, but when you check the fine print, sugar is often in the first group of ingredients. Sometimes our attention is diverted by claims of 'fortified with', reassuring us of vitamins that have been added and convincing us it must be healthy. So what to do when you're craving a breakfast grain on your way out the door?

Oats are a brilliant alternative. They are high in fibre, protein and carbohydrate, and also provide an array of vitamins and minerals. Oat groats are the least processed and take the longest time to prepare, whereas 'instant' oats are, as the name suggests, the quickest to prepare but are the most processed. Our go-to oat is rolled, but you can also get crushed and steel-cut, all of which sit somewhere in between for both prep time and the amount of processing they've been through.

We love our oats eaten cold as bircher muesli or overnight oats, hot in porridge/oatmeal or baked into bars, muffins and cookies.

Rice

Opt for brown, red, black or wild options instead of white wherever possible. Brown rice is more nutritious than white rice and contains significantly more fibre. It has a slightly firmer and nuttier texture and takes a little longer to cook. Enjoy exploring the subtle differences in flavour between basmati, jasmine, long grain and wild. Cooking times vary, so always check the guidelines on the side of the pack or do an online search on how best to cook that particular type. As brown options take longer to cook, remember to start the process a little earlier. Many times it's the first step in our overall meal prep.

We love rice in risottos, poke bowls, salads and as a side dish to curries, chillies and burrito bowls.

Pasta

If you can tolerate gluten, whole wheat pasta is a good option in lieu of white. Our favourite is brown rice pasta, which is a popular and naturally gluten-free alternative that has a similar texture to white pasta. However, there are a number of others available made from different grains and pulses, like chickpea, corn, multigrain and lentil. Check the contents and if you can, opt for versions that don't have any other added ingredients. As with rice, cooking times vary and alternative grain/pulse pastas can go from al dente to mushy very quickly. It's worth setting a timer, staying close to the pan and tasting to get familiar with the amount of time it takes to cook to your desired texture.

We love pasta in homemade vegetable sauces, bakes, power bowls and salads.

Noodles

As well as containing white flour, often labelled 'wheat flour', some types of noodles also contain eggs. Soba noodles are a naturally gluten-free alternative, made of buckwheat, which despite the name, does not contain wheat. Yes, we think it's confusing too! Some brands may sneak in other flours, so look for 100% buckwheat options. Brown rice noodles are another great choice and are available in thin vermicelli as well as wider, flat varieties.

We love noodles in pad thai, salads, soups and stir fries.

Bread

Bread is something of a national treasure, with every country, or even region having its own speciality. As a result, breads come in a vast range of shapes, sizes, and flavours, with plenty of grain choices. Loaves, rolls, bagels, wraps, flatbreads, sweet, savoury, salty, dense, light, chewy, soft – you name it, bread's got it covered.

A global staple, and often readily available from a bakery or supermarket, the humble slice has evolved into one of the most convenient and versatile foods around. Ease and convenience mean that bread can form the base of breakfast, lunch or dinner.

For most people, bread is not inherently bad. However, too much of one thing isn't always a *good* thing. Because of its many guises, we can unwittingly consume the same grain at every meal: toast for breakfast, bagel for lunch and burritos for dinner. That's wheat bread three times a day, and possibly more depending on snacks like crackers, biscuits and pastries.

 Try to be mindful of the grains you are eating throughout the day. If you are using bread as a base more than once, consider choosing a variety of different grains (wheat, rye, oat, flax etc) and different preparation techniques such as sprouted or sourdough.

Just as not all grains are created equal, neither are all breads. Those made with whole grains - the ones that keep the 'whole grain' – maintain the goodness nature intended for us to benefit from and enjoy. With so many types of breads and flours available, how do we distinguish the good, the bad and the ugly? Names might vary significantly from country to country, but there are a few consistent labelling terms to help you identify breads that can provide you with the vitamins and fibre they were intended to.

- 100% whole grain. When the whole grain is left intact, the outer layer of bran remains. It is this part of the grain that is high in fibre, good for the gut and gives us that lasting feeling of satisfaction. If you can, avoid options that list 'wheat flour' as the main ingredient. It may seem counterintuitive, but wheat flour is made using only the endosperm, the starchy central part of the grain. The germ, the vitamin-rich part, and the bran, the fibre-rich part, are removed, resulting in a less nutritious option. If you are scouring the shelves, know that ingredient labels list food in order of quantity, making ingredients easier to spot.

- Fortification. Beyond the main grain, look at the rest of the ingredients list. Usually this will tell you just about everything you need to know. It might sound crazy, but because vitamins are removed along with the germ in the processing of wheat flour, bread manufacturers then fortify them, by adding *back* nutrients. For example, in the UK it is the law to fortify white and brown wheat flour by adding iron, thiamin, and niacin.[74] The UK is not alone in this practice. As these nutrients come hand in hand with wheat flour, check to see if there is a 100% whole grain option available or choose one that lists a whole grain first.

- Added extras. Bread can be a hidden source of sugars and oils that are often buried in a sea of words, brackets, commas and asterisks. Take a look at what else is in there.

- Gluten-free. These are breads made without the main gluten containing grains; wheat, rye and barley. If you're looking for a gluten-free option, always check the ingredients list or ask the baker. Typically gluten containing allergens will be highlighted in bold in the ingredients list. Whilst 'gluten-free', like the term 'vegan', can imply a healthy alternative, they can be packed with refined flours and sugar. There are some amazing, naturally gluten-free seed bread recipes both online and in cookbooks that don't take hours to make. In the 'Resources to Inspire You' section, we've listed some of our favourite cookbooks and food bloggers that you might like to explore.

For most people it's not harmful to eat bread, but we should all be aware of just how much we are consuming, as bread is the master of disguise. Look for whole grains wherever possible, and mix up the types of grains to give your taste buds and your body a variety of flavour, texture and nutrients. It's a chance to dig out that bread maker you have tucked at the back of your cupboard, or have a go at making your own for the first time. There are a multitude of recipes online to suit every taste, and many aren't nearly as time consuming as you might expect.

We love bread as a sandwich, avocado on toast and with soup.

Danish rugbrød

In Denmark, rye bread, or to give it its proper name, rugbrød, is king. Slices of this rich, dark bread form the foundation of the country's infamous smørrebrød. Traditionally, these open-faced sandwiches are topped with meats and fish, but these days there are more and more plant-based options available. Studies have found that eating rye bread for breakfast leads to decreased feelings of hunger after both breakfast and lunch, especially when compared to wheat bread.[75]

Other grains

We've only scratched the surface in terms of the more commonly eaten grains and we encourage you to browse the shelves of your local store to see what else is on offer. Don't feel obliged to buy them all, or even one. See what your options are, go home, do an online search for a recipe with a new grain and add it to the list for the next time you go shopping.

Here are a few grains to look out for:

- Millet
- Bulgur
- Amaranth
- Couscous
- Quinoa
- Cornmeal (polenta)
- Barley
- Sorghum
- Teff

Preparation guidelines vary for each grain, so make sure to check the package or go online for cooking instructions. Remember to always give grains a thorough rinse before cooking. We both use a fine mesh strainer to avoid too much waste. No one wants to see their grains get washed away!

Legumes, Pulses and Beans

Can you tell your bean from your legume from your pulse? Though the terms are often used interchangeably, they aren't the same. So before we go any further into the types and uses of these plant-based protein powerhouses, let's start with distinguishing the difference between them.[76]

- A legume is a plant from the Fabaceae family and includes the leaves, stems and pods. The important thing to remember is that it is the *plant*. A good example is a pea pod.

- A pulse is the edible seed from a legume plant. Examples of pulses include beans, lentils and peas.

- Beans are just one type of pulse. Examples of beans include chickpeas, kidney, black, cannellini, pinto, adzuki, etc. We love beans and promise more on these later.

Pulses have been a nourishing part of the human diet for thousands of years and they are increasingly making a name for themselves on national food guidelines in countries with meat-centric diets. This is due both to their high protein and fibre content and their reduced environmental impact (compared to meat). With the wide variety of colours, flavours and textures, pulses make for a versatile addition to any plant-based meal.

Protein-Packed Pulses

It's well-documented that pulses are a valuable source of protein, iron and fibre as well as a host of additional vitamins and minerals. However, just as important as what they do contain is what they don't. Compared to meat, which contains both cholesterol and saturated fat, pulses have neither. What's more, many studies support the cholesterol lowering impact of including pulses in your diet.[77] We could write a whole book singing the praises of the humble bean, but our main aim is to help you find achievable and delicious ways to add some of the more readily available pulses into your meals and snacks.

You might not think of tofu as a pulse, but as it originates from soybeans and is made from condensed soy milk, it qualifies. Tofu has a wonderful versatility, and we both like to view this plant-based staple as a blank canvas that can be prepared, flavoured and cooked to shine as the star of any cuisine. Over the years it has received a lot of press regarding its health and environmental impacts, emanating from the use of Genetically Modified Organisms (GMO) grains. We encourage you that when possible, choose tofu that is organic and non-GMO. Tofu primarily comes in two forms: silken and firm. Silken tofu can be a great addition to soups, while firm tofu is great in stir fries, and even a good alternative to meat on the grill, seasoned with your favourite BBQ seasoning. It can take some time and experimentation to get used to working with tofu and finding the meal and flavour combinations that work for you. But don't give up, this great source of protein really is a workhorse!

Preparation and Packaging

Depending on how they are prepared, pulses can be a speedy meal addition, especially great for those busy weeknight dinners. Lentils are relatively easy, they can be rinsed and cooked pretty quickly. Straight from a tin, beans can be drained and enjoyed as they are, or reheated as part of a hot meal. If you are using dried beans, they'll need a few additional steps. The process may take time, but the effort involved is minimal. Preparation guidelines vary from bean to bean, so check the packaging or if you are unsure, search online for cooking guidelines. Cooking from scratch also cuts down on food waste, as you only prepare the quantity you need. It can also be a more sustainable option when it comes to packaging, reducing the quantity of tin cans.

Dips and Spreads

One of the most popular pulse dips is the loveable hummus. This chickpea-based dip is easy to make and is also readily available in shops and on menus. In fact, this versatile plant-based solution to pasta sauce, sandwich filling, cracker and salad topper, and accompaniment to crisps and crudites is so popular, we're starting to hear about "hummus-fatigue".

To avoid over-dependence, switch up your ingredients. Try using beetroot, basil or red bell pepper to add colour and different flavours. Or try spicing it up by mixing in some chilli, paprika, harissa or cumin to bring some heat. To keep things interesting, use different pulses as a dip base. Lentils, black beans, fava beans, cannellini beans; there's a dip for them all. Whole beans with sweetcorn and tomato used as a salsa, or blended with garlic and spices, with all the choices of texture and flavour, there is something to suit just about every cuisine.

Burgers and Balls

Once you find a good base recipe, you can shape it or size it to fit different occasions. Black beans, for instance, are ideal for adding depth of colour, whilst the smooth nature of white beans makes them easy to mash or blend. Here are just a few ideas:

- Fashioned into burgers in buns for barbeques.
- Served as a patty with sweet potato wedges and salad.
- Rolled into balls and paired with a tomato sauce atop a bowl of spaghetti.
- Stuffed into a salad-laden pitta as falafel.
- Providing the protein in a delicious salad bowl.
- The main event, with steamed vegetables and brown rice.
- Sliced tofu, marinated or crumbed, and baked or pan cooked.

Chillies, Curries, Stir Fries and Stews

In meals where you may have traditionally used meat, like curries and stews, beans stand out as a star substitute, effortlessly transitioning your meal from meat-based to plant-based. The firm bite of beans provides the meaty texture that many look for when making a change.

Slow cook recipes in particular pack a punch when it comes to flavour. Don't be afraid to use a different variety if you don't have the exact pulse the recipe calls for. In fact, part of the fun is experimenting, finding the flavours and textures that work for you!

- Instead of mince, use lentils in your next spaghetti bolognaise.
- When it comes to chilli, the more the merrier with beans. Buy them already mixed or create your own concoction. We love recipes that include a bit of dark chocolate, it adds both a richness of colour and depth of flavour. Looking for ways to use a big batch of chilli? Try:
    - with rice or corn bread
    - in wraps to make burritos
    - in taco shells
    - as a topping to baked sweet potatoes
    - baked with tortillas, for the ultimate loaded nachos
    - as a burrito bowl

    and of course, none of these recipes would be complete without some fresh tomato salsa and guacamole.
- Try Pad Thai, a tofu classic with noodles, vegetables, and peanuts dressed in a sweet, spicy and salty sauce.
- Stir-fry with vegetables, a simple sauce and serve with noodles for a quick and easy weekday meal.
- Replace the meat or fish in your favourite Thai curry with tofu.
- Use your lentils to make a yummy dal, which stands alone or alongside other curry dishes.
- For less heat but still plenty of flavour, add beans to root vegetables to make a warming stew.

Salads, Sandwiches and Soups

We've both been left hungry and less than impressed by limp and lacking salads. We believe that salads should leave you feeling super-charged and satisfied. Between the protein and the fibre, adding pulses to your salad will help banish those bouts of mid-afternoon or post-dinner munchies. Try:

- Mezze bowl – add a spoonful of your favourite dip, a few falafel with lots of leaves, cucumber, tomato, olives and artichoke.

- Mexican inspired bowl – mix black beans and sweetcorn together with paprika, cayenne or chipotle (or all of them if you like it spicy!), add some rice or quinoa, and add a dollop of salsa and guacamole on top.

- Quesadillas make for a speedy light meal or snack. Non-dairy cheese, black or kidney beans, and for extra colour and flavour, some sliced peppers, mushrooms and sweetcorn.

- For a homemade take on a British classic, make your own baked beans with cannellini beans, chopped tomatoes and some smoked paprika. Serve warm with a couple of slices of whole grain toast. Comfort food zen!

- Spicy black bean, minestrone, miso, lentil are all tasty soups that will leave you feeling oh so satisfied.

Meat Alternatives

With the astronomical rise in awareness, availability and purchase of meat-alternatives, the value of the global plant-based and cell-based meat market is anticipated to be US$252bn by 2030.[78] Brands like Beyond Meat are riding what's been called 'the lean, green, money-making machine'.[79] There is no doubt that meat-free alternatives are helping reduce the over reliance on meat in our global food industry by giving meat eaters an alternative and introducing some to a more flexitarian approach. However, it's important to remember that meat substitutes are processed alternatives, which means they have additional ingredients added to them. The quality and quantity of these ingredients vary, so we encourage you to opt for ones with recognisable ingredients and minimal additions of salt, oils and sugars. One sense check we use a lot is to ask ourselves if we would use those ingredients if we were making a meal at home. It's not that long ago that soy-based products were the only alternative. Now there's a plethora of pulse and vegetable options out there. Some even use beetroot to mimic the juice of a meat burger! If you're interested in a plant-based experience that mimics a meatier one, try a few and see which you like best. We'd encourage you to enjoy them like you would any other processed food, occasionally and whole-heartedly!

Nuts and Seeds

Nuts

Attitudes to nuts run the gamut, from being hailed as a superfood to being villainised for fat levels. In truth, nuts *do* have a high fat content, but most contain the 'good' fats, monounsaturated and polyunsaturated. We need some fat in our diet to keep us healthy, it's an important source of energy, helps us absorb some vitamins and minerals and it is vital for a number of essential processes including muscle movement.[80] If your body can tolerate nuts, they are an incredible source of protein and fibre, which is why they leave us feeling satisfied.

It's easy to munch on a few nuts as a snack but there are many other ways to add nuts into your meal times. To get the most nutritional benefit from nuts, it's best to eat or use raw or toasted versions, rather than salted. For the technical readers, there are a few nuts that are actually classified as seeds, such as cashews, and some as legumes, like peanuts. For ease, we've grouped them into the nuts category, as this is generally how they are best known.

Nut Butters
A quick word on nut butters. In an ideal world, everything would be made from scratch, but we both know that in reality, some things are easier to buy. Very occasionally we make our own nut butter as it's helpful to familiarise ourselves with the ingredients needed for a fresh batch. This way we can spot the added extras on the ingredients label when we're buying a jar. When choosing a shop bought nut butter, look for options with the fewest ingredients and the highest percentage of nuts. In fact, some are made with 100% nuts. Avoid those with added sugar and palm oil when possible. As nuts are themselves a source of oil, added oils are not essential. Many have a little salt added to enhance the flavour. As always, it comes down to personal preference and what's available to you.

Go Nuts!

Be adventurous and mix your nuts! This way you'll reap the benefits of different types. Whole, chopped or smooth, here are a few ideas to add energy-giving nuts to your meals:

Breakfast ideas:

- Stir in a spoon full of nut butter or sprinkle some chopped or whole nuts onto your porridge, overnight oats, coconut yoghurt or chia pot.
- Blitz a spoonful of nut butter into your smoothie or smoothie bowl.
- Make your own granola with toasted nuts. Homemade lets you customise to find your perfect combination.
- Spread some nut butter onto a slice of whole grain or seed bread. For a touch of sweetness, slice a banana on top.

Lunch and dinner ideas:

- Blitz some peanut butter into a satay or pad thai sauce and stir into noodles.
- Sprinkle some cashews into a stir fry.
- Bring a salad to life with a jam jar salad dressing. Add some nut butter, olive oil, lemon juice and for a kick, a sprinkle of chilli flakes or cayenne pepper, then shake to combine.
- For the ultimate nutty meal, it doesn't get nuttier than a nut loaf. This is a great replacement for roasted meat, especially for holiday or celebration meals.

Snacks

- Make a trail mix by combining your favourite nuts, seeds and dried fruits.
- Add some spice to nuts by dry frying in a pan or toasting in the oven. Sprinkle on some paprika or cayenne pepper for a savoury hit, or cinnamon or vanilla to bring some sweetness.
- Spread some nut butter on slices of apple.
- Combine nuts with dates, cacao and chia seeds to make chocolate energy balls.

Sow the Seeds

These are some of the ways we enjoy seeds at different meal times:

Breakfast ideas:

- Sprinkle pumpkin and hemp seeds onto your porridge.

- Power up a smoothie bowl by adding chia and ground flax seeds and topping with pumpkin and hemp seeds.

- Make a breakfast-on-the-go chia pot in a jar by stirring together chia seeds and plant milk. Leave overnight and top with fruit the next morning.

- Try making your own seed bread, many recipes out there don't require kneading or proofing which makes preparation time much shorter.

Lunch and dinner ideas:

- Sprinkle some pumpkin and sunflower seeds onto your salad or power bowl.

- Sprinkle some sesame seeds onto Eastern-inspired dishes.

- Bring a salad to life with a jam jar salad dressing. Add some tahini, olive oil, lemon juice and for a kick, a sprinkle of chilli flakes or cayenne pepper, then shake to combine.

Snacks

- Make a trail mix by combining your favourite nuts, seeds and dried fruits. Leave out the nuts to make it nut-free, and for a chocolatey hit, add some cacao nibs.

- Add some spice to seeds by dry frying in a pan or toasting in the oven. Sprinkle on some paprika or cayenne pepper for a savoury hit, or cinnamon or vanilla to bring some sweetness.

- For a sweet treat, stuff dates with tahini.

- Try some nut-free, no-bake energy balls with oats, seeds and a little maple syrup.

Seeds

They may be small but they are mighty! Seeds are one of the newest and biggest additions to our food, and are an equally nutrient-dense alternative to nuts. Like nuts, they are a valuable source of protein, 'good' fats, fibre, and important vitamins and minerals. Some of our favourites are chia, hemp, pumpkin (also known as pepitas), sunflower, sesame and flax (also known as linseeds). The shells of flax seeds are not easily digested by humans so one way to use them is to grind them in something like a coffee grinder before adding them to your food. Omega-3 fatty acids are healthy fats vital for many processes like helping to reduce inflammation[81] and supporting brain health.[82] Our body doesn't naturally produce them so we need to get them from our diet. Chia, hemp, pumpkin and flax seeds are all great plant sources of omega-3s in place of the more widely known sources of fish and fish-oils.

Seed butters too are starting to appear on the shelves. Tahini is probably the most familiar and the most readily available. Made from sesame seeds, it serves as a brilliant alternative to nut butters in both sweet and savoury recipes. For us, it's been particularly useful for making nut-free packed lunches for school!

Spice Up Your Life

If your herb and spice rack is a little neglected, it won't be for much longer. These leaves, roots and powders don't just elevate the taste of your food to a whole new level, each has incredible healing properties. For centuries, herbs and spices have been used for medicinal purposes, here are just a few reasons why:

- Cinnamon can lower blood sugar levels and decrease inflammation.[83]

- Turmeric contains curcumin which is known for its powerful anti-inflammatory effects. However, to really experience the benefits it needs to be combined with black pepper, as it's this addition that improves the absorption rate of curcumin by 2000%.[84]

- Ginger appears to have anti-inflammatory properties and can also act as a pain reliever.[85]

- Garlic can help reduce blood pressure in those experiencing high blood pressure.[86]

Sometimes we choose to add certain herbs or spices for their healing benefits but mainly it's just because they make food so much more interesting and enjoyable!

Poornima's Experience: Yellow Gold

I grew up hearing about the amazing health benefits of "haldi doodh" (translated from Hindi: turmeric milk) from my grandmothers, family and friends and later on, even from my grandmothers-in-law. Turmeric is a spice that's integral to Indian cooking, for flavour and colour but more importantly for its incredible health benefits. Everyone in the Indian diaspora seems to know that the secret to health lay in this golden powder, a secret that was passed down from generation to generation. Because I'm intolerant to cow's milk, I had to find alternative ways of enjoying turmeric in the food I cook and also as a drink. Today, I love a good pinch of turmeric, a dash of black pepper and a squeeze of lemon juice in warm water. It's a taste that took a little getting used to, but I love knowing that I am helping my body deal with inflammation in a natural way.

The Spice of Life
Be adventurous adding herbs and spices to your meals; these are just some easy the ways we love to bring the flavour:

Breakfast ideas:

- Mix in some cinnamon and/or cardamom to your porridge or overnight oats.

- For a warm and filling breakfast, our savoury pancakes are made with coriander, cumin and chilli.

Lunch and dinner ideas:

- Make pesto with fresh basil.
- Add some chilli flakes to guacamole.
- Sprinkle paprika, cayenne pepper and chipotle chilli onto black beans and sweetcorn for a smoky and spicy addition to tacos.
- Chop up some garlic and ginger to liven up your greens.
- Add some garlic and herbs to homemade soups.
- Chillies, curries and stir fries are a guaranteed way to add in a variety of flavours. Poornima is the queen of spices and has shared some of her favourite authentic Indian and Asian dishes throughout the book.

Snacks

- Sip on a warming drink laden with spices like a turmeric latte or masala chai.
- Dry roast or toast nuts and seeds in sweet or savoury spices.
- Bring your hummus to life by adding different herbs and spices. Add basil for a sweet flavour, or cumin or harissa for warmth.
- For a sweet and spicy treat, try our sweet squares.

Moo-ving On

For us, not consuming dairy was one of the most challenging aspects of going fully plant-based. In the last five years, we've both discovered that we are highly intolerant to dairy, something we both long suspected, but had confirmed through a blood test. Seeing the results in black and white certainly helped motivate us to avoid foods containing dairy, but we found that once we started studying ingredients labels, it was surprising just how many foods contained some form of milk.

Plant Milks

Vivienne's Experience: Spoilt for Choice

The first time I heard about oat milk was about nine years ago and it felt like a totally alien concept. It's funny to think that nowadays, it's the norm. In fact, I've seen so many different types of plant-milk on restaurant and cafe menus in various countries around the world.

I was never a big milk drinker but I did have it in drinks. For me, switching to soy milk was the easiest way to start removing dairy. Looking back now, I'm not sure why I accepted soy milk so easily and yet questioned it coming from other sources. Occasionally I'd forget to request an alternative milk and by default be given cow's milk. I could almost immediately tell the difference in taste and texture, but it was the instant gurgling in my stomach that made me aware of its impact on my body.

It has been trial and error working out which flavours and brands of plant-milks I prefer in different meals and I've found that rather than choosing one, I like to have a variety. My family have been a part of my milk journey though they have a definite firm favourite, oat milk!

With the sheer number of plant milks in the chillers and on the shelves, we are spoilt for choice and no longer need to rely solely on soya milk. Each plant milk has its own flavour and consistency that lends itself to different uses. We recommend trying them to see which you prefer in your hot drinks, oats, smoothies, cooking and baking. We love hazelnut milk in hot chocolate and oat milk in coffee. Oat milk is also a great choice for keeping a recipe nut-free. In our kitchen fantasies, where we have unlimited time and energy, we would make our own plant milk, but for now, we choose convenience. When you are perusing your options, look for a short and simple ingredients list to make sure there are no added extras like oil or sugar. You may also like to consider if it's organic and therefore free from GMOs (Genetically Modified Organisms), and responsibly sourced.

 Did you know that soya milk has been a staple in the Chinese and Japanese diet since the 11th Century; though some sources put it even earlier?

Poornima's Experience: Milk and Me

My relationship with milk has been a rollercoaster. I've certainly come a long way since my childhood days of throwing up after every glass of cow's milk. When I began to suspect that cow's milk was making me feel ill, I switched to soya milk. While it's much easier today to find various plant milk options in many parts of the world, that wasn't always the case. A decade ago, soya milk was the only plant milk available and even then it was challenging to find when I was travelling as it wasn't as popular in Europe as it was in Asia, where I lived at the time.

Even though soya milk was widely known and readily available, it didn't stop the constant comments from family and friends who questioned my choice not to drink cow's milk. When I was pregnant with my children, well-meaning family members worried my unborn child wasn't getting adequate nutrition because I wasn't consuming cow's milk and its products. To be honest, sometimes I was more exhausted from the need to explain myself than I was from actually carrying a baby inside me! Thankfully, with increased awareness and wider availability of plant milks, these comments have reduced.

About five years ago, fed up with playing guessing games with my food choices and body, I took an intolerance blood test. Turns out that I am not just lactose intolerant but casein (milk protein) intolerant as well. Knowing this was somehow liberating and comforting all at the same time. I finally had proof of what I had suspected for a long time.

Spreads

Dairy-free spreads have been around for some time, think of the margarine push of the 1970s, but recently there has been an overhaul in their quality. Products like margarine were created to be a cheaper alternative to butter, and many contained artificial trans fats (also known as trans fatty acids) which have been found to be harmful to our health.[87] As a result, some countries have banned them, whilst others have called on food companies to reduce them. They will appear as 'partially hydrogenated oil'[88] or 'mono and diglycerides of fatty acids'.[89] Be mindful of these when you're checking the ingredients list. Other things you can look out for are ingredients from sustainable sources, or the inclusion of nuts in some brands.

Yoghurt

As the plant milk range extends, so too does the range of yoghurts. In many places you can now choose from almond, coconut and oat options. As with regular dairy yoghurts, keep an eye on the sugar content. Our absolute favourite alternative is coconut yoghurt. We buy it plain and then top it with fresh fruit or fruit compote, nuts and seeds. Customising our own toppings makes it a personal treat, as well as keeping the sugar content down.

Dairy-Free Cheese and Nut Cheese

Are you struggling with the thought of not having cheese? You're not alone and as it turns out, there may be a good reason why we love cheese. Dr Neal Barnard, author of *The Cheese Trap*,[90] believes that cheese has an opioid-like effect on the brain. Casein, the protein found in milk, becomes highly concentrated during the cheese making process. When it's digested, the casein is broken down and additional components called casomorphins are released. These attach to the same brain receptors as heroin and other narcotics. Researchers believe this is nature's design to keep calves coming back for more milk, to ensure their survival. When this concentration is increased, as it is with cheese, the effect is intensified as well.[91]

The good news is that if you decide to wean yourself off cheese, there are other ways to satisfy the taste you might crave. There are readily available dairy-free cheeses that cover most bases; blocks, slices, grated and spreadable. Generally speaking, dairy-free cheeses are highly processed, so we'd encourage you to use them sparingly, say as a topping to dishes like tacos.

When it comes to the classic cheese board, there's a new kid on the block: the artisan nut cheese. These little works of art look remarkably similar to their dairy counterparts and don't look out of place next to some crackers and grapes, or on a mezze plate. They are increasingly accessible online and in artisanal stores, but they are also relatively easy to make at home with a good blender. Cashews, almonds and Brazil nuts are some of the most frequently used.

Nuts aren't just used to make cheese, you will also find them in many classic recipes that call for a creamy texture. You can use cashews to recreate many of your family favourites, like mac n cheese, carbonara, ranch dressing and bechamel sauce as well as cream itself. If you're avoiding cashews or nuts in general, sunflower seeds can be used as a substitute in some savoury dishes.

One of our new favourite ways to bring a cheesy flavour to our dishes is by using nutritional yeast. We're not going to lie, the first time we opened a package of nutritional yeast, we were underwhelmed. But before you make a judgement, give it a try. It is pretty versatile and can be used in sauces, soups, dips, tofu scramble, egg-free omelettes, risottos and even sprinkled onto popcorn to offer both a cheesy and nutty addition. And, as a source of protein and vitamin B12, it has more to offer than just flavour.

Live Well, Live Long

Vivienne's Experience: Making it Count

During my studies, I came across a thought-provoking statement: We are "living shorter and dying longer". Statistically, our life expectancy has increased,[92] but with the continued rise in chronic diseases, these extra years aren't necessarily healthy, active ones. Since hearing this phrase, I haven't stopped thinking about ways in which we can make sure we are living longer and dying shorter, starting with making sure we're taking care of our bodies and minds.

Like you, we want to make the most of being fit, healthy and loving life, for as long as possible. To end this chapter, and perhaps nudge you a little further along the way, we wanted to share the incredible discovery of the BLUE ZONES.[93] The Blue Zones include five regions, in five different countries across four continents where the highest number of centenarians or those with the highest life expectancy have been found. These extraordinary places include:

- Barbagia region of Sardinia
- Ikaria, Greece
- Nicoya Peninsula, Costa Rica
- Seventh Day Adventists in Loma Linda, California
- Okinawa, Japan.

Researchers have identified a combination of nine lifestyle characteristics, consistent across the people in these regions. Perhaps you won't be surprised to learn that one characteristic is a predominantly plant-based diet. In fact, it's close to 95% plant-based.[94] This plant-based diet is rich in all the foods we have outlined in this chapter including pulses, whole grains, nuts and seasonal fruits and vegetables. In addition to a healthy, plant-plentiful diet, here is the full list of what the researchers and demographers term, the POWER 9:[95]

1. They get their exercise from their everyday movement.
2. They have a sense of purpose, a drive that gets them out of bed in the morning.
3. They have stress management strategies built into their daily routine. Practices vary by region and include reflection, prayer, naps and happy hour.
4. Their last meal of the day is the smallest and they eat until they are 80% full.
5. Plant-based foods form the basis of all their meals and they favour pulses as their source of protein.
6. Wine is enjoyed both frequently and moderately, with the company of others.
7. A sense of belonging is fulfilled through being part of a faith-based community.
8. Relationships with their partner, children and parents are prioritised.
9. They have strong friendships with like-minded people who help shape their health behaviours, for the better!

These BLUE ZONE communities are living proof of just how powerful our lifestyle choices are, and just how much power we have when it comes to the ability to shape our own health and well-being.

SCRAMBLED TOFU

Serves 4 people; Nut free

If you're scrambling for a wonderful way to ease yourself into plant-based breakfast and brunch options, this tofu recipe is just the ticket. Spice it up with chilli and red onion and serve on whole grain toast.

1. Place a frying pan on medium heat. Once hot, add the oil. Fry the onions and green chilli on low to medium heat for 4 minutes until soft.

2. Add the tomatoes and cook for 3-4 minutes or until softened.

3. Reduce to low heat. Add the turmeric powder and stir. Then add the tofu. Stir well. Mash the tofu with the back of a spatula.

4. Add salt to taste.

5. Serve hot on toasted bread.

1 teaspoon oil

1 small red onion, finely chopped

¼ – ½ green chilli, finely chopped

½ tomato, finely chopped

3-4 pinches of turmeric powder

600g silken tofu, drained

Salt, to taste

TURMERIC LATTE

Serves 1 person; Nut free

A supercharged kickstart to your day, this popular Indian beverage is a great way to fight inflammation while enjoying something warm! Don't skimp on the black pepper, it helps your body absorb the benefits of turmeric.

1. Put the turmeric, black pepper and cinnamon in a mug.

2. Warm the coconut or oat milk in a pan or in the milk frother of your coffee machine.

3. Pour over the turmeric mixture and stir. Sweeten if needed.

¼ teaspoon turmeric

Good pinch of crushed black pepper

Good pinch of cinnamon powder

200ml light coconut milk or oat milk

POKE BOWL

Serves 1 person; Nut free option

We haven't met a poke bowl we didn't love. This one is bursting with a rainbow of flavour and colour, and is a fantastic way to use all those grains, veggies, and seeds you have in your kitchen. And don't forget to go "nuts"!

1. Cook your choice of grain as per the package instructions.

2. Place the edamame beans in a small saucepan with water on medium to high heat and boil for 10 minutes.

3. For the dressing, add the ingredients to a blender jar and blend well.

4. Assemble the poke bowl ingredients in a big bowl starting with the grains at the bottom.

5. Serve with dressing on the side or drizzled on the top.

Poke bowl

30 g dried grain of your choice like bulgur/cous-cous/oat rice/spelt/brown rice

40g frozen edamame beans

35g red cabbage

25g carrots, chopped

20g beetroot, julienned

20g baby spinach leaves

80g cooked chickpeas

20g sunflower seeds and pumpkin seeds

Salt, to taste

Pepper, to taste

Dressing

1 tablespoon tahini paste (sesame paste)

2 teaspoon rice vinegar/white vinegar

1 tablespoon tamari/soy sauce

1 tablespoon olive oil

40ml hot water

½ teaspoon maple syrup

Pinch of salt

ROASTED RED BELL PEPPER AND CUMIN HUMMUS

Serves 4 people; Nut free

If you love hummus but are looking for something new, the addition of roasted red pepper in this recipe is a great way to really boost the flavour factor.

1. Preheat the oven to 200℃. Place the red bell pepper on a baking tray and make 2 slits in it with a knife. This is to release the steam as the pepper roasts.

2. Roast the red bell pepper in the oven for 30 minutes.

3. Remove from the oven and leave to cool. Pull the inner stem with the seeds off from the top tip. Peel the skin, and chop the flesh into big chunks. Reserve any liquid aside to be used when blending.

4. Add the red bell pepper, chickpeas, garlic, olive oil and 1 tablespoon of the reserved liquid to a blender jar. Blend. Add more water (a little at a time) only if needed, the hummus should be smooth, thick and creamy.

5. Stir in the cumin and salt.

6. Put into a serving bowl and drizzle with olive oil. Serve with your favourite crackers or chopped vegetables. You can also use it as a spread on rye bread, topped with your favourite vegetables to make a meal.

1 red bell pepper, washed

240g cooked chickpeas

1 clove garlic

2 tablespoons olive oil plus more to drizzle on top at the end

1 tablespoon of water (use only if needed)

2 teaspoons cumin powder

Salt, to taste

SWEET POTATO AND KALE SALAD

Serves 4 people; Nut free

A colourful and delicious salad that packs a nutritious punch and makes eating your veggies a breeze. We love the contrast of bright orange against fresh spring greens and the bite of roasted kale in every mouthful.

1. Preheat the oven to 200°C.

2. Place the kale in a large bowl, toss in 2 tablespoons of olive oil and salt, and spread evenly onto a baking tray.

3. Place the sweet potato in a bowl, toss in ½ tablespoon of olive oil and salt, and spread evenly onto a baking tray.

4. Place both the kale and sweet potato in the oven (with the kale on the bottom rack) and bake for 25 minutes.

5. In the meantime, place the remaining ingredients into your salad bowl.

6. Once the kale and sweet potato are ready, remove from the oven and cool fully on the baking tray. This is really important for the kale to crisp up.

7. Add the kale and sweet potato to the salad bowl, add salt and pepper and drizzle with olive oil just before serving.

150g kale leaves, washed and dried

2 medium sweet potatoes (approximately 220g), peeled and cut into thick, circular discs

75g baby spinach

75g rocket leaves (arugula)

100g cherry tomatoes, sliced in halves

2 avocados, sliced

1 tablespoon pumpkin seeds

1 tablespoon sunflower seeds

Olive oil

Salt, to taste

Pepper, to taste

MISO SOUP

Serves 4 people; Nut free

A little bit of Asian-inspired flavour has never been easier to bring to your table. Add some udon noodles and you've got yourself a nourishing meal. We promise we won't tell if you slurp until the bottom of the bowl!

1. Place a large pot on medium heat. Add the water, miso, ginger and tamari, stir well and bring to the boil.

2. Add the spring onions and bok choy/enoki mushrooms. Reduce the heat to low and simmer for 10 minutes.

3. Add the tofu. Simmer for 2–3 minutes on low heat. Be careful not to stir too much as it will cause the tofu to break.

4. Serve hot, garnished with spring onions.

1500ml water

3 tablespoons brown miso paste

1 tablespoon ginger, chopped or grated

2 ½–3 teaspoons tamari/soy sauce (depending on preference)

50g bok choy or enoki mushrooms, with the ends chopped off

300g silken tofu, drained and cut into 2cm cubes

50g/2 sticks spring onions, chopped (set a little aside as a garnish for each bowl)

Handy tip: You can add some boiled noodles – we like udon noodles – to the soup to make it a complete meal. Place your cooked noodles in a bowl, top with the soup and enjoy.

RAINBOW NOODLE SALAD

Serves 4 people

This crowd-pleaser isn't just delicious, it's packed with a rainbow of fresh vegetables. Experiment with your favourites, this is one case when it really is the more the merrier. A great picnic dish to share or to savour all by yourself.

1. Add the dressing ingredients to a blender jar and blend until smooth. If the mixture is too thick, add a little hot water. Set aside.

2. In a large bowl, add the noodles and vegetables. Toss with the dressing. Add the coriander, spring onions and crushed peanuts. Add salt and pepper as needed. Give it a good mix and it is ready to serve.

For the dressing

2 tablespoons tamari/soy sauce
2 tablespoons tahini paste (sesame paste)
2 tablespoons smooth peanut butter
60ml hot water
2 tablespoons lime juice
2 tablespoons orange juice
1 teaspoon Tabasco or your favourite hot sauce (optional)

For the salad

300g buckwheat soba noodles or whole wheat spaghetti, prepared according to package instructions
100g carrots, julienned
1 red bell pepper, julienned
1 green bell pepper, julienned
1 yellow bell pepper, julienned
5 tablespoons spring onions, chopped
6 tablespoons coriander leaves and stem, chopped
6 teaspoons peanuts, crushed (optional)
Salt, to taste
Pepper, to taste
Feel free to mix the vegetables up. You can add snow peas, red cabbage or any of your favourites.

RICE PAPER ROLLS

Serves 2–4 people; Makes 8 rolls

Some days your body wants light and fresh, and that's where our Rice Paper Rolls come in. Zingy, crunchy delights, these rolls make a wonderful appetiser or even a light lunch.

1. Place the glass noodles, vegetables, spring onions, coriander, mint and chilli into a bowl and mix well with the tamari.

2. Place a damp kitchen towel on a plate ready for the rice paper rolls. This will prevent them from drying out before you serve them. Have another damp kitchen towel ready to cover the rice paper rolls as you make them.

3. Fill a large bowl with warm water.

4. Put a rice paper roll into the warm water and let it soften for about 20 seconds.

5. Transfer your softened rice paper rolls onto a chopping board. Place about 2 tablespoons of your filling - depending on the size of your rice paper roll – closer to the bottom of the circle. Roll.

6. Place the completed rice paper rolls on the damp kitchen towel, and cover with another damp kitchen towel.

7. Repeat for the remaining rice paper rolls.

8. Serve them whole or cut them in half. Serve with tamari/soy sauce with some white sesame seeds, or your favourite chilli sauce.

50g glass noodles, cooked as per the package instructions

50g carrots, julienned

50g sugar snaps/ cucumber, julienned

2 stalks spring onions, chopped

2 tablespoon coriander leaves, chopped

1 tablespoon mint leaves, chopped

½ – 1 red chilli, chopped fine (optional)

1 tablespoon tamari/ soy sauce

8 rice paper rolls

Handy tip: Take a look at the image below to help you with rolling your rolls. It is important to keep the filling and folding as tight as possible.

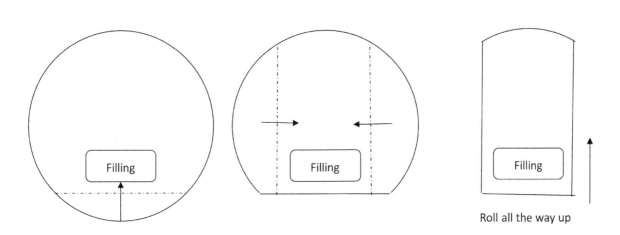

Roll all the way up

GREEN GOODNESS PASTA

Serves 2 people; Nut free

*Our kids call this the 'Hulk' pasta, and whenever we make it,
it's always a mealtime hit.*

1. Place a frying pan on medium heat. Once hot, add the olive oil. Fry the garlic and leeks on low to medium heat for 5 minutes until leeks are soft.

2. Add the baby spinach and cook until it wilts. Add a splash of oat milk. Mix well and take off the heat and leave to cool.

3. Add the leek and spinach mixture to a blender jar. Blend until very smooth, adding a little water if needed.

4. Put the blended leek and spinach mixture into a pan on low to medium heat, add salt and stir.

5. Add the pasta and stir until evenly coated.

2 cloves garlic, crushed

2 leeks, slice the pale green part into thin, circular discs

60g baby spinach leaves or frozen spinach cubes defrosted

1 tablespoon olive oil

Splash of oat milk

Salt, to taste

250g pasta, boiled and drained as per package instructions

HEARTWARMING STEW

Serves 4 people; Nut free option

If you're looking to spice up your life, look no further than this North African inspired dish. A combination of rich, flavourful spices, sweet dates, and star anise is guaranteed mouth-watering goodness. Serve with warm pita bread, brown rice or couscous for a body and heartwarming meal.

1. Place a large pot on medium heat. Once hot, add the oil. Fry the onions and garlic on low to medium heat for about 5 minutes until the onions have softened.

2. Add the turmeric, coriander, cumin, cinnamon and paprika/chilli powders, and the star anise. Fry for half a minute on low to medium heat.

3. Add the tomato paste/purée and tomatoes. Mix well.

4. Add the eggplant, zucchini, green beans, walnuts and dates. Add the water and salt. Give it a good stir to mix everything well. Bring to the boil on medium to high heat. Reduce to medium heat and simmer for about 6 minutes.

5. Add the chickpeas. Stir and continue to simmer on medium heat for another 10 minutes.

6. Serve with warm whole wheat pita, brown rice or couscous.

1 tablespoon oil

1 large red onion, chopped

4 cloves garlic, whole

1 teaspoon turmeric powder

1 teaspoon coriander powder

1 teaspoon cumin powder

½ teaspoon cinnamon powder

¼ to ½ teaspoon paprika/chilli powder

1 star anise

1 tablespoon tomato paste/purée

5 tomatoes, quartered

2 medium aubergines/eggplants (about 530g), cut into big chunks

1 medium courgette/zucchini (about 275g), cut into ½ cm thick semi-circles

100g green beans, cut into 5cm long pieces

50g walnuts

5 dates, chopped roughly into big chunks

500ml water

Salt, to taste

240g cooked chickpeas

SWEET POTATO FRIED RICE

Serves 4 people; Nut free

Next time you find yourself reaching for the takeaway menu, try your hand at our super quick and easy fried rice instead. A plate-painting family favourite!

1. Place a large frying pan on medium heat. Once hot, add the oil. Fry the onions, garlic and ginger on low to medium heat for 4–5 minutes until the onions have softened.

2. Add the sweet potato and a little water. Cook until the sweet potato is soft.

3. Add the bok choy and cook until it softens.

4. Add rice and soy sauce. Mix very well. Adjust the flavour by adding more soy sauce or salt to taste.

5. Serve hot, garnished with spring onions.

1 teaspoon sesame oil

1 small red onion, finely chopped

1 clove garlic, finely chopped

1 teaspoon ginger, peeled and grated

2 small or 1 medium sweet potato, peeled and cut into small cubes

2 bunches bok choy, chopped (use baby spinach if bok choy isn't available)

300g brown or white jasmine rice, cooked as per package instructions and cooled

2 teaspoons tamari/soy sauce, or to taste

Salt, to taste

1 tablespoon chopped spring onions

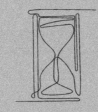

Take
YOUR TIME

"It's never too late to start eating well."
- T Colin Campbell

elebrities like Beyonce and Kim Kardashian have challenged their fans to try it. Lewis Hamilton and Venus Williams support it. The World Health Organization recommends it. From research to media coverage to celebrities, at times it feels like you can't turn your head without reading about the benefits of a plant-based diet. And for good reason. In addition to the WHO, the United Nations also recommends that we adopt a more plant-based diet not just for the good of our bodies, but our planet as well. As a global community, there's never been more awareness that our food consumption habits have an impact on the planet.

With so much information and so many different terms, it can be overwhelming. How does plant-based differ from vegan or vegetarian? What does a pescitarian diet look like? And what is a flexitarian anyway? If you're confused, you're not the only one.

Let's clear it up.

Vegan Diet

egans and veganism certainly get a lot of press, both good and bad. Strict vegans consume only plant-based products and avoid all animal products, including honey, fur and leather goods. Understandably, this may seem like a drastic lifestyle change if you are dipping a toe into making changes for environmental or health reasons. A word of warning, however. Whilst a purist vegan diet includes plant-based products, with the increase in the diet's popularity, there has been a rise in heavily processed vegan foods. Though ostensibly designed to make it easier to adopt a vegan lifestyle, these products are chock full of refined sugars and fats, so if inclined, please consume such products with caution.

Vegetarian Diet

he term vegetarian dates back to the 4th-6th century and has both cultural and religious roots. *Vegetarian* is used to describe anyone who doesn't eat meat and fish, but unlike vegans, vegetarians often do consume dairy and eggs. The addition or omission of dairy groups leads to further variations in identification: lacto-ovo (dairy-eggs), lacto- (dairy) and ovo- (eggs) vegetarian. Does this seem confusing to you? It does to us, and while *vegetarian* is sometimes used as a blanket term to describe anyone who doesn't consume meat and fish, there seems to be a desire for more precise labels to define our food habits.

Flexitarian Diet

A relative newcomer to the diet and lifestyle family, flexitarians are those who exercise the choice to adopt plant-based meals most days of the week and yet occasionally eat meat and fish. This lifestyle is most closely aligned to the 'planetary health diet' recently reported in The Guardian[96] as the first science-based diet to take into consideration both personal health and global impact. According to a recent study by *Nature*,[97] a flexitarian diet is defined as one that includes:

- At least 500g per day of fruits and vegetables of different colours and groups (the composition of which is determined by regional preferences)
- At least 100g per day of plant-based protein sources (legumes, soybeans and nuts)
- Modest amounts of animal-based proteins, such as poultry, fish, milk and eggs
- Limited amounts of: red meat (one portion per week), refined sugar (less than 5% of total energy), vegetable oils that are high in saturated fat (in particular palm oil) and starchy foods with a relatively high glycaemic index

David Yeung, co-founder and CEO of Green Monday, suggests that the flexitarian approach is appealing to many because: *"If we make it an all-or-nothing binary situation, most people may simply decide to take a pass due to their own inertia or their unaccommodating social or family environment"*.[98]

Plant-based Diet

P lant-based seems to be all the rage these days, with supermarkets across the world sprouting a growing variety of plant-based and meat-alternative products. The term "whole foods plant-based" was coined and made famous by Prof. T. Colin Campbell,[99] researcher and author of the most comprehensive nutritional study ever undertaken, *The China Study*. Prof. Campbell suggests that a plant-based diet is one that is based primarily on plants, including vegetables, whole grains, nuts, seeds, legumes and fruits. He recommends avoiding animal protein, and refined or processed foods.

It's possible that as a term, plant-based is more appealing and inviting, perhaps because it does not have the same association with rigidity as the term vegan. While vegan and vegetarian seem to have connotations of removing something from a meal, plant-based seems to conjure up an image of adding nourishment to your body.[100] A plant-based meal is a vegan meal, but a person following a plant-based diet may not be a vegan. Throughout this book, when we have referred to the term plant-based, it's in reference to a whole food plant-based diet.

 Plantier's Definition of a Plant-Based Diet: A plant-based diet is one that includes vegetables, fruits, grains, nuts and legumes from plant sources that are minimally processed, and that avoids all animal products including dairy, meat, fish and eggs. Where possible, this also means using seasonal and fresh produce.

In 2019, approximately 400 million people had adopted plant-based diets,[101] and the number is growing. GlobalData estimates that 70% of the global population is either reducing meat consumption or avoiding meat entirely.[102] According to the Plant Based Food Association, one-third of Americans are actively reducing their meat and dairy consumption and flexitarians represent the largest growth opportunity for plant-based foods.[103] These numbers help illustrate just how many people around the world are making changes to their food habits, with health and socially responsible consumption topping the list of reasons why.

Regardless of the food 'label' you may or may not choose to adopt, one thing is for sure, our plates need more fruit, vegetables and whole grains!

"So What?": The Evidence-Action Disconnect

*F*ood is an integral part of our existence as humans, not just physically, but socially as well. From memories of a family reunion digging into our grandmother's curry, to the enjoyment of hosting a dinner party with friends, food brings us together. It may bind us to a culture or a religion, region or community. Food choices are also deeply personal. As you consider embarking on a journey towards plant-based food, you may find that your personal food choices become part of the public conversation. You may be confronted with barriers. Some of these barriers arise from within us, while others are external. We feel that understanding what these barriers are and why they might arise is a key step in helping you along your personal path.

Despite global consumer trends shifting in favour of plant-based diets, despite the rise in the number of plant-based food manufacturers offering us greater and tastier choices, despite the clear call for action by doctors and scientists, a lot of us still struggle to change our food choices.

It's not easy. In fact, quite the opposite. As we move towards eating more sustainably, one tool at our disposal is trying to understand where the resistance to change comes from. Some cite eating routines, health conceptions, enjoyment of meat, and perceived difficulties in preparing plant-based foods as barriers.[104] These barriers are strongly linked. That is, we may not recognise enough of the differences between them, which can make the barriers seem even more unsurmountable.

So how do we overcome these barriers? We have found that an approach which embraces *knowing them*, *acknowledging them* and *addressing them* is the best way to move forward.

We believe that there are six main barriers to adopting more plant-based meals. Let's break them down together.

Barrier #1: Cultural Traditions

The link between food and culture is deeply entwined. The world over, communities bond over food, and every society prides itself on their unique cuisine. Food is also a great way to get to know and understand a culture, as food is often integrated with traditions and practices. For the Western world, eating turkey at Thanksgiving or a roast pig at Christmas are deeply rooted cultural practices. Switching to plant-based alternatives can seem strange and counterintuitive. In some cultures meat consumption is not just a dietary preference, but also a reflection of status and wealth, and it might seem inconceivable not to serve meat at special occasions like festivals and wedding banquets.

Barrier #2: Generational Gaps

There also appears to be a *food generation gap* between baby boomers and millennials. The former were raised post World War II, during a period of food scarcity and significant changes to food production. They grew up believing and being told that cow's milk was the best source of nutrition (in particular, calcium for healthy bones) and that meat was essential for protein and growth. Millennials, on the other hand, are redefining what 'eating healthy' means. They favour food that is natural, organic, locally sourced or sustainable, and, it would seem, are the driving generation towards plant-based and plant-forward eating, followed by Gen Z, Gen X and then the Boomers.

Nonetheless, the millennial-led push by students towards more plant-based diets seems to be gaining ground across an increasing number of colleges and universities, who have entirely or partially removed animal products from their cafeteria menus. They include (among others) the University of Cambridge, Oxford University, Goldsmith, University of London, University of California, and a growing list of colleges who are now part of a "Meatless Monday" movement.

Fiona Dyer, a consumer analyst at GlobalData explained: *"The shift toward plant-based foods is being driven by millennials, who are most likely to consider the food source, animal welfare issues, and environmental impacts when making their purchasing decisions."*[105] Health seems to be the motivator for baby boomers,[106] while environmental impact and animal welfare are the motivating factors for millennials and Gen Z consumers.[107] Regardless of reasoning, we are certainly seeing a generation shift. 60% of Gen Zers want to eat more plant-based foods and 79% of them are already eating plant-based 1–2 times a week.

Barrier #3: Cognitive Dissonance

In her book, *Why We Love Dogs, Eat Pigs, and Wear Cows: An Introduction to Carnism*,[108] social psychologist Melanie Joy introduces *carnism*, the belief system and psychology of meat eating. Carnism, according to Joy, is the driving, dominant force supporting the choice to eat meat in modern culture. Joy believes that the choice to eat meat is strongly influenced by social conditioning. Despite meat-eating tendencies, the majority of people, Joy claims, care deeply about animals and don't want them to suffer.

In societies where it is hard to find a concrete link between the food they eat and its environmental impact, eating sustainably can seem like an abstract idea to be addressed by future generations, with people believing that their individual actions are too insignificant to make any difference. In highly urbanised cities where agricultural activity is not visible, citizens eat three to five times more meat and eggs[109] than is environmentally sustainable. This mental disconnect, or *cognitive dissonance*, between the food on our plates and how that food is grown or produced, has many underlying causes including geography, socio-economics and education levels.

Barrier #4: Negative Associations

There is a subtle but important difference between a plant-based diet and veganism. People following a plant-based diet do not consume animal produce, but may still choose to use it in other areas of life such as clothing, accessories and toiletries. Vegans, on the other hand, do not consume or use any animal produce. Often, but not always, this decision is based on views regarding animal welfare and rights. Unfortunately, there are sometimes negative assumptions concerning those who practise veganism and consume vegan diets, and their personal choices are sometimes perceived to be politically motivated or activist in nature. The negative perceptions and stereotypes may be shaped in part by extreme cases in which vegan activists have engaged in violence, threats and disruption towards farmers, journalists, restaurants, supermarkets and other establishments.

Poornima's Experience: Living in a Bubble

Having lived in Singapore for most of my life, I had not really paid attention to where the food on my plate was coming from. Thanks to my Mom's amazing cooking, I have always enjoyed nutritious vegetarian food filled with fresh vegetables and fruit. And I always thought that was enough. Until I moved to Copenhagen, I had very limited understanding about the environmental impact of my food choices. Driving through dairy and rapeseed farms, and picking fresh strawberries and tomatoes at farms in Denmark made the connection between the food on my plate and the environment more real. That was enough for me. I began my quest to learn more about the impact of our food choices on the environment. Sometimes it's hard to believe something until you see it.

Barrier #5: Misinformation

With more people embracing greener diets, many food manufacturers have capitalised on this growing consumer group by introducing a deluge of "vegan-friendly" foods aimed at making it attractive for consumers to jump on the vegan bandwagon. However, many of these fail to contribute to improved health of our planet or our bodies and are high in sugar and fat, or highly processed, and should really be known as "vegan junk food". This has led to some skepticism about the true and actual benefits of vegan and vegetarian diets.

Barrier #6: Dining Out

We all love a nice *hygge* (Danish for cozy) meal out with family and friends, enjoying great food and lovely company. When you're considering incorporating more plant-based options in your meals, choosing where to eat and what to order can seem daunting and can even be a deterrent. After all, no one wants to be met with blank stares from waitstaff or be made to feel like an inconvenient customer.

Dismantling Barriers: A Holistic View

We truly believe a shift needs to take place in the way we consume food, both on a smaller individual level as well as a larger, global one. Getting more people on board with plant-based eating won't be easy. It will take consistent and concerted efforts by governments, corporations, media groups, the food industry and, perhaps most importantly, individual consumers. At state and policy levels, politicians and activists have suggested setting national carbon reduction goals for the food industry, imposing carbon taxes, or charging businesses for pollution. Health ministries of countries also have the responsibility to verify the credibility of research sources, modify dietary guidelines and push for plant-based knowledge to be shared actively. In this regard, Canada is leading the way. The country has updated its dietary guidelines to promote plant-based diets, and citizens are encouraged to replace most animal proteins and fats with plant-based

Vivienne's Experience: Great Adaptations

A few years ago my family generously gave me a voucher to dine at an iconic restaurant that I had been desperate to go to. I excitedly made the booking, letting them know that I was plant-based and double checking there would be some options on the menu for me. A very courteous lady reassured me it would not be a problem; she would let the chef know in advance, and I would have a choice of dishes to choose from on the day.

With great expectations, I opened the menu to find... nothing I could eat! When I asked our server, she kindly pointed out all the ingredients they could remove from the one starter and one main that most closely resembled a plant-based meal. Disappointed, I gave them the benefit of the doubt, hoping that the chef would be able to create something more exciting than a salad and plate of vegetables. Sadly, when my food arrived it was just that. There it was, a sea of plain lettuce leaves with a few raspberries scattered across the top to break up the green. The main did include three types of vegetables. What it didn't include was any protein or carbohydrates. Two dishes later, I was hangry! Right then I made a vow to do more to raise awareness of plant-based food in the hospitality industry. I'm happy to say that with Poornima and Plantier, this has become more than just a vow.

sources. On the flip side, in the EU there has been public and political debate about the labelling of non-dairy milk as 'milk' as well as the imposition of additional taxes on plant milk. In Germany, for example, plant milk bears a 19% value added tax (VAT) and is classified as a luxury food, while cow's milk carries only a 7% VAT surcharge.[110] This does seem to be discriminatory towards people with lactose and casein intolerances, financially punishing them. Regardless of what we call our plant-based staples, we need to see more of them on our supermarket shelves and in our kitchens, to be inclusive to consumers' needs, preferences and choices.

In the business space, corporations can require that caterers provide substantial and appealing plant-based options at the workplace, thus reducing both their carbon footprint and offering employees the nutritional benefits of plant-based meals. Green Monday, a Hong-Kong based organisation, has been hugely successful in inspiring more players in the corporate sector to introduce "green Mondays" in their staff canteens.

The media, in its varied platforms, can also play an important role. By giving more airtime to content that discusses the impact of animal agriculture and meat consumption on the planet, more awareness can be built. Responsible reporting is imperative, and will go a long way towards combating the misrepresentations and inaccurate stereotypes that surround plant-based eating.

Finally, the food industry and its players – caterers, chefs, grocers and restaurateurs – play a significant role. By improving consumers' access to plant-based food, whether at home or when dining out, they can really help move the needle.

We should push for our institutions, companies and governments to take well-being seriously. After all, the health of the planet is at stake. But beyond that, what can you do as an individual?

We're glad you asked.

Starting with YOU: One Step at a Time

*W*hile the need to fight climate change is urgent, for changes in our food choices to stick and avoid boomeranging back to old habits, it's crucial to approach this as a gradual shift rather than an immediate swing. That way it's likely it will be less overwhelming and more sustainable for the long run. In this regard, flexitarianism, also referred to as "semi-vegetarianism", might be a great place to begin.

According to *The Flexitarian Diet*[111] by Dawn Blatner, the beginner flexitarian eats 6 to 8 meatless meals a week, an advanced flexitarian 9 to 14, and the expert at least 15 meatless meals a week. A flexitarian diet is varied, but includes plenty of fruits and vegetables, plant-based proteins from legumes, lentils, beans and nuts, modest amounts of poultry, fish, milk and eggs, and small amounts of red meat.

The Planetary Health Diet,[112] based on the EAT-Lancet study, similarly recommends that we eat half a plate of fruits, vegetables and nuts; the other half should consist primarily of whole grains, plant proteins (pulses), unsaturated plant oils, modest amounts of meat and dairy, and some added sugars and starchy vegetables.

Vivienne & Poornima's Experience: Fed Up

We understand how difficult it can be when dining out. In fact this was the very reason for us setting up Plantier. After many meals out of grilled asparagus, kale and carrots (yes, we know that grilled asparagus is quite the delicacy), we were desperate to get restaurant owners and chefs to think creatively about making substantial and delicious plant-based meals. Meals that tasted good and filled us up. We weren't fed up with food, but we were fed-up with being the joke at the table, the one others looked at with pitiful eyes, while everyone else enjoyed a hearty meal. Of course there are some cuisines that lend themselves to plant-based options, like Mexican, Thai, Chinese and Indian. But we were also conscious of being "that" family member or friend, the one who was always "dictating" the restaurant choice.

In Denmark, a study conducted by the Dansk Vegetarisk Forening (Danish Vegetarian Association) revealed that a lack of suitable dining-out options was the top barrier preventing people from eating more plant-based foods.[113] Those findings certainly meshed with our own experiences.

Luckily, things have improved. With the growing number of customers who are adopting dairy-free, egg-free, meat-free diets or some combination of those, the food industry has had to start paying more attention. Apps like abillion and HappyCow use customer reviews to help customers find restaurants with plant-based options near them, helping to build a community around plant-based dining.

Eating out was difficult for us until we learnt to take a bit of control. So if you're eating out and can't see anything on the menu, just ask. Sometimes the restaurant will have a separate menu or the chef will make you something. When going to someone's house for a meal, inform the host in advance and offer to bring a dish that you can eat. Often, people will respond by saying that they would be happy to make something for you. In fact, most hosts have told us they were happy we spoke up! We understand how annoying and uncomfortable it can be – at office social events or parties – to be the only person who requires a different meal. We still feel that way occasionally. At the same time, awareness has increased and people are less critical of others' food choices. You may even find they are interested to know more.

> *If there is one thing we have learnt, it is to be unapologetic about our choices. We are strong in our conviction that a plant-based diet is good for the planet and our bodies. So the next time you dine out, hold your head up, and ask for a plant-based meal or side or dessert. You might be surprised, especially if no one blinks an eye.*

It's difficult to break away from well-established food habits. The very idea can seem daunting. But armed with the right know-how, support and recipes like the ones we've shared, making planet-friendly, plant-based swaps is something we can all aim towards. Suzy Amis Cameron, the author of *OMD: The Simple, Plant-Based Program to Save Your Health, Save Your Waistline, and Save the Planet,*[115] provides a practical guide to changing the world by the simple act of changing one meal a day. It's a bite-sized solution we can all sink our teeth into.

In her book, Suzy suggests that eating just one plant-based meal a day for a year will save 736,895 litres of water and 350 kilograms of carbon emissions. If we increase that to three plant-based meals a day for a year, we would save the equivalent of the amount of greenhouse gases generated from driving from New York to San Francisco...four times. Moreover, *"If everyone in the world consumed a predominantly whole food, plant-based diet, nearly 5 billion football fields of land could be restored to forest."*[116] This restoration of forests is a crucial step to reversing the effects of climate change.

A collective mindset shift starts from an individual decision. There are natural and economic circumstances that may make it difficult or impossible for the world's population to commit to a plant-based diet, but for those who are ready to make a conscious switch, nothing is more important than taking that first step.

Give yourself time and space to think about your own goals. Start with something small, a change that requires minimal effort but has a positive impact. You might start by removing cow's milk from your tea and coffee; swapping them with plant milks like almond or oat or you may find you enjoy your tea or coffee without any milk at all! It might be easier to make a plant-based meal rather than give up cheese. Your journey will be your own. Remember, every meal makes a difference – do what you can – whether it is one meal a week, or one meal a day. It may take you some time to get used to the changes you're making, but the impact on your health, and the health of the planet, will be profound.

Crowding Out

How many times have you said "I will never eat/drink/do that again!" after an over-in-dulgence or even a new resolution? Of course, once you've made this bold statement, you can usually think of nothing but exactly what it is you've just sworn off. 'Never' is a strong word, one that heaps the pressure on us to deliver, and as we all know, circumstances sometimes prevent us from keeping a promise or resolution, no matter how well-intentioned. Going 'all in' can feel like the quickest route to success and reaching your goals, ripping the band-aid off so to speak. Swift, even if it's painful, often feels more achievable when com-pared with slow and moderate.

Most of us have grown up hearing the words, 'everything in moderation'. In fact, we've prob-ably uttered them ourselves from time to time. In principle the idea is easy. In practice? Not so much. How much *is* moderation? These limits are personal and we need to find the bal-ance that works for us.

Vivienne's Experience: Crowding Out

When it comes to moderation, one of the most effective tools I've come across is the idea of crowding out. It is a concept I learnt during my studies with the Institute of Integrative Nutrition, and has helped many of my clients make sustainable habit changes. It can be applied to any aspect of your life that you would like to change, be it food or drink related or any other behaviour.

In essence, crowding out is the decreasing of one thing by simultaneously increasing something else in its place.

Say you want to stop or just reduce the amount of dairy you consume. You might want to start with just one form of dairy, in this case, milk. First, you could make a list of all the times you have milk throughout the day, perhaps on your breakfast cereal and in your tea or coffee. One place to start would be to try different plant milks on your cereal to see which you prefer. Once you feel comfortable in making this swap, you might want to test some alternatives for your hot drinks. You might find one that you really like (we've found that oat milk in coffee is often a winner). Equally, you may discover that the alternatives just don't cut it. In this case, you might try something totally different, a drink that doesn't require milk like herbal teas, or just drinking more water. You might decide that rather than giving up your milky drink, you make it a weekly treat rather than daily. You have "crowded out" your dependence on milk by introducing an array of alternatives. This takes away the pressure of *never again* and replaces it with a gradual shift towards your goal, at a pace that works for you.

Activity: Your Step-by-Step Guide to Going Plant-Based

Are you ready to take your first step? Here is an easy to follow guide to start adding more plant-based options into your weekly meals. The important thing to remember is there's no right or wrong way to add more sustainable food to your life, and this is a great opportunity to be honest about what you're hoping to achieve on your journey. Take a moment to think about what changes you'd like to make. Be optimistic, but realistic. Take your time, and aim for progress, not perfection.

Step 1: Reflect.
Visualise what your ideal food lifestyle looks like and describe it here.

....
....
....
....
....
....

Why do you want to move towards plant-based food habits?
Be specific and honest. You may be doing it for your own health or the health of the planet, or perhaps both.

....
....
....
....
....
....

Step 2: Identify where you are now.

Are any of these plant-based options already part of your week? If so, which ones?

- ☐ Drinks including tea/coffee
- ☐ Breakfast
- ☐ Lunch
- ☐ Dinner
- ☐ Snacks
- ☐ Dessert

Step 3: Plan where you'd like to go.

Do you have an idea of which meals you'd like to be plant-based? Remember, your goals are always your own. They should be achievable and within reach. Keep your lifestyle and circumstances in mind; trying to do too much too soon can be frustrating.

- ☐ Drinks including tea/coffee
- ☐ Breakfast
- ☐ Lunch
- ☐ Dinner
- ☐ Snacks
- ☐ Dessert

How long are you willing to give yourself to achieve your first goal?
Keep in mind your own lifestyle and individual circumstances, and be kind to yourself!

_____weeks _____ months _____years

Step 4: Select one drink or meal of the day to start with.

When you're choosing which drink or meal to start with, keep in mind the time it takes to prepare, and which options are well-suited for change. For instance, if you're used to eating at the company canteen, your options might be limited, and you may find it difficult. But if you are used to eating cereal for breakfast, switching out your regular milk for plant-milk might be an easy swap to make. Pick an option that requires the least amount of effort but has enough impact to make you feel like you are on the way to achieving your goals.

Step 5: Create a food plan for that drink or meal for 3 weeks.

Developing new habits and changing our behaviour takes time. Commit to 21 days. That's doable, right? Of course it is! We've provided you with delicious, easy recipes along the way and a meal planner to help you prepare. We've given you the nudge, all that's left is the first step.

Step 6: Ready, set, go!

You're on your way! It might help you to keep a log so that you can track how you're feeling, physically and mentally. And if you forgot to order your latte with plant-milk one day, it's ok. Be kind to yourself. Give yourself time and space to remember why you took this step in the first place.

Step 7: Reflect, adapt and power on.

How did you do?

....

....

....

....

....

....

....

....

....

....

....

What's holding you back?

....

....

....

....

....

....

....

....

....

....

....

....

....

....

....

....

Maybe you feel like it's too hard to give up something you love, like a particular dessert or your favourite cheese. Maybe you're worried about what others will think or being the odd one out in social situations. Identify what's stopping you from moving towards your goals. We all have barriers. We've been there; we understand.

When you're ready, simply go back to Step 3 and explore your next option. Remember, progress not perfection. Every journey starts with the first step, and we're right there with you.

WARM QUINOA OAT PORRIDGE

Serves 4 people; Nut free

Oats porridge hot, oats porridge cold, oats porridge in the pot...There's nothing better on a cold, winter day than a bowl of porridge to warm the body and soul.

1. Place the quinoa and water in a small pot and bring to a boil on a medium to high heat. Reduce heat to low and simmer for 10-12 minutes.

2. Add the oats and oat milk, increase the heat to medium and bring to a boil. Lower the heat and simmer for 5-7 minutes.

3. Add the sugar and stir. Adjust the consistency with some additional oat milk if needed.

4. Divide into bowls and serve topped with berries and bananas, and even some of our homemade Granola Munch if you have it handy.

2 tablespoons quinoa, rinsed thoroughly under running water in a mesh strainer for a few minutes to remove the bitter outer coating

400ml water

90g oats

350ml oat milk

3 teaspoons coconut sugar

1 large banana, sliced

Fresh berries

Additional oat milk

MINT AND CORIANDER CHUTNEY

Makes a jar; Nut free

We're addicted to this fresh, aromatic chutney made with fresh coriander, mint and ginger. Whizz it up lickety-split and serve as the perfect accompaniment to our savoury chickpea toast.

1. Put all the ingredients into a blender jar. Blend well until smooth.

2. Pour into a jar and enjoy with rye crackers, brown rice cakes or as a spread for sandwiches. Store in the fridge for 2–3 days.

50g coriander leaves, washed and drained

60g mint leaves, washed and drained

2 tablespoons ginger, roughly chopped

2 tablespoons lemon juice

½ large green chilli (optional)

4 tablespoons water

1 teaspoon salt, or to taste

SAVOURY
CHICKPEA TOAST

Serves 4 people; Nut free

Ooh la la! This savoury take on French Toast gets its kick from your spice cupboard. Served with our mint and coriander chutney, you'll savour every bite.

1. Place the chickpea flour, onion, coriander leaves, tomato, cumin, chilli powder and salt in a mixing bowl.

2. Add the water and whisk well to remove flour lumps (a few lumps are fine). Let it rest for 20 minutes, then whisk again.

3. Place a frying pan on medium heat. Once hot, add a thin layer of oil. Dip a slice of bread into the chickpea batter and fry on low to medium heat, flipping once the underside is golden brown. Once both sides are golden brown, remove and blot on a kitchen towel. Repeat for the other slices of bread.

4. Serve hot with ketchup, or chutney and a nice cup of tea.

150g chickpea flour (also known as gram flour)

1 small red onion, finely chopped

2 tablespoons coriander leaves, chopped

1 tomato, finely chopped

1 teaspoon cumin powder

¼ teaspoon chilli powder

½ teaspoon salt

350ml water

Cooking oil

8–10 slices of bread, cut in half

Ketchup or mint and coriander chutney

MASALA CHAI

Serves 1 person; Nut free

Nothing beats a hot beverage in the morning. This Masala Chai is bound to warm you from the inside out and is a wonderful way to introduce those small changes that make a big impact.

1. Place all the ingredients in a small saucepan on medium heat and bring to the boil. Reduce heat to low and simmer for 6 minutes.

2. Strain into a cup and serve immediately. Sweeten if needed.

200ml oat milk

275ml water

1 English breakfast tea bag or 1 teaspoon loose black tea (Darjeeling or Assam work best)

1 ½ teaspoons ginger, cut into big chunks

4 green cardamom pods

4 black peppercorns

2 cloves

¼ cinnamon stick

LEEK SOUP

Serves 4 people; Nut free

This hearty soup could not be easier to whip up, making it the perfect option for those busy days and nights. A satisfying family favourite, serve with warm bread and enjoy!

1. Place a large pot on medium heat. Once hot, add the olive oil. Fry the garlic on low to medium heat for half a minute.

2. Add the chopped leeks and fry until soft, this should take about 5 minutes.

3. Add the vegetable stock and thyme. Bring to a boil on medium heat. Lower heat and simmer for 10 minutes. Add salt and pepper to taste. Blend with a hand blender until smooth.

4. Serve with warm bread.

1 tablespoon olive oil

3 cloves garlic, sliced or crushed

3 leeks, slice the pale green part into thin circular discs

2 cubes of vegetable stock, dissolved in 1L of hot water

1 tablespoon dried thyme

Salt, to taste

Pepper, to taste

CHILLI OIL
SILKEN TOFU

Serves 4 people; Nut free

Easy to make, tasty to eat, this cold Indonesian-inspired dish will really spice things up.

1. Place the silken tofu in a bowl and mash with the back of a fork until the tofu is fully broken down. Add salt and set aside.

2. Place a small frying pan on medium heat. Once hot, add the sesame oil. Add the whole dried red chillies or dry chilli flakes and fry on medium heat until the chillies brown slightly for about 1–2 minutes. If using whole dried red chillies then you may need to fry for a minute longer.

3. Pour the sesame oil and chillies onto the tofu. Garnish with the spring onions. Serve with rice or noodles, and your favourite vegetable stir fry like our Stir Fry Broccoli/Broccolini. Sprinkle some white and/or black sesame seeds on your rice or noodles for some extra nourishing goodness.

600g of soft silken tofu, drained

Salt, to taste

2 tablespoons sesame oil

3–5 whole dried red chillies or 1–2 teaspoons of dry chilli flakes (depending on your spice level preference)

3 stalks spring onions, finely slice the soft parts

STIR FRY
BROCCOLI/BROCCOLINI

Serves 4 people; Nut free

Crunchy, crisp, and cruciferous! This stir fry is simple to make, but full of flavour. Use broccoli, broccolini, or swap out for any vegetable you have in your crisper. It makes a great accompaniment to Dry Chilli Tofu or Chilli Oil Silken Tofu.

1. Place a large frying pan on medium heat. Once hot, add the oil and fry the garlic and ginger on low to medium heat for 1 minute until softened.

2. Add the broccoli florets/broccolini and tamari/soy sauce. Add a little water if needed. Cover and cook on medium heat until just soft and tender, about 10-12 minutes. Adjust salt to taste. Serve with wedges of lemon.

1 teaspoon oil (we like sesame oil but any cooking oil will do)

3 cloves garlic, sliced thinly

2 teaspoons ginger, julienned or grated

400g broccoli florets/broccolini

1 tablespoon tamari/soy sauce

Salt, to taste

3-4 wedges of lemon

CURRIED
BUTTERNUT SQUASH

Serves 4 people; Nut free

This Sri Lankan inspired curry squashes the competition. Starring spice cupboard staples and creamy coconut milk, every mouthful is an explosion of flavour.

1. Place a large pot on medium heat. Once hot, add the coconut oil. Fry the onions, ginger and garlic on a low to medium heat for 5 minutes until the onions are soft.

2. Add the curry powder. Fry for 30 seconds on low heat.

3. Add the coconut milk and water. Increase heat to medium and bring to a simmer. Simmer for 3–4 minutes.

4. Add the butternut squash, potato and bell pepper. Cook on medium heat for 8 minutes. Add the mushrooms, tofu and salt, and cook for a further 15 minutes. Check that the butternut squash is cooked through; cook for a few more minutes if needed.

5. Garnish with the red chilli, coriander leaves, spring onions and lime. Serve with white jasmine rice or brown rice.

1 tablespoon coconut oil

2 medium red onions, chopped

1 tablespoon ginger, grated

3 cloves garlic, crushed

4 teaspoons store-bought curry powder

800ml light coconut milk (or 400ml coconut milk and 400ml water)

400ml water

250g butternut squash, peeled and cut into 2 cm cubes

1 medium potato, peeled and cut into 1 cm cubes

1 green bell pepper, cut into 2cm cubes

100g button mushrooms, sliced

250g firm tofu, cut into big cubes

Salt to taste

½ red chilli, sliced (optional)

1 lime, sliced into 4 wedges

2 tablespoon coriander leaves, chopped

1 stalk spring onions, chopped

ZUCCHINI BURGER

Serves 4 people; Nut free

Garden goodness in the form of a 'burger' patty. Grated zucchini (courgette) is the star of this delicious and nutritious meal, described by one dear friend as "the best plant-based burger I've ever tasted!".

1. Place the grated zucchini in a large mesh strainer placed on top of a large mixing bowl. Add about 1 teaspoon salt. Mix and leave for 20 minutes.

2. Use a potato masher to press the water out of the zucchini. Remove as much water as you can.

3. Place zucchini in a large, dry mixing bowl. Add the spring onions and about 350g of the breadcrumbs and mix well. Check seasoning. Add more breadcrumbs if needed. The zucchini should be sticky and easily shaped into patties.

4. Put remaining breadcrumbs into a wide, shallow bowl.

5. Take a handful of the zucchini mixture and shape into a thick patty. Coat with the breadcrumbs on both sides.

6. Place the patties on a large plate and place in the fridge for 30 minutes.

7. Place a large frying pan on medium heat. Add oil for shallow frying. Once the oil is hot, reduce to a low to medium heat and add the patties. Shallow fry the patties in the oil until each side is light brown (you can also fry it without any oil for a healthier option).

8. Spread plant-based mayonnaise on both sides of a burger bun. Add ketchup on the one half.

9. Place a lettuce leaf on the bottom half of the burger bun. Top with the zucchini patty, a few onion rings and cover with the top half of the burger bun.

4 medium zucchini/courgette, grated

2–3 stalks spring onions, finely chopped

500g breadcrumbs, homemade or store-bought

Salt, to taste

Oil for shallow frying

6–8 burger buns, sliced in half

Plant-based mayonnaise

Ketchup

1 small red onion, sliced into thin rings

Lettuce leaves

MASALA CHICKPEAS WITH SPINACH

Serves 4 people; Nut free

Our go-to dinner party dish, this easy to prepare but complex in flavour meal is packed with protein. Served with rice or naan, this Indian inspired meal is one of our favourites.

1. Place a large pot on medium heat. Once hot, add the oil. Fry the onions, ginger and the whole green chilli on a low to medium heat for 8 minutes until the onions are soft and browned.

2. Add the tomatoes and the turmeric, coriander, cumin and garam masala powders. Fry on low to medium heat for a minute. Add 150ml water and mix well. Cook until the onion-tomato mixture is very well cooked and soft. It should be mushy with most of the water dried up.

3. Add the chickpeas, spinach and salt. Add the remaining 150ml of water. Mix well and cook on medium heat for another 10 minutes or until the water has evaporated.

4. Serve, garnished with coriander leaves, with warm naan (Indian bread) or white/brown basmati rice.

1 tablespoon oil

1 large red onion, chopped

1 tablespoon ginger, julienned

1 whole green chilli, make a small slit

3 tomatoes, chopped

1 teaspoon turmeric powder

1 teaspoon coriander powder

1 teaspoon cumin powder

1 teaspoon garam masala*

¼ teaspoon chilli powder

300ml water

75g chopped fresh baby spinach (you can also use chopped frozen spinach, defrosted)

750g cooked chickpeas

Salt, to taste

Coriander leaves to garnish

* Garam masala is an Indian spice mixture, widely available in supermarkets.

Handy tip: If using chickpeas out of a can or package, save the liquid. In the plant-based world, this is known as aquafaba and is often called 'liquid gold'. Aquafaba can be used as an egg white substitute in recipes. Use an electric whisk to whisk until it becomes frothy and firm. As a rough guide, three tablespoons of aquafaba will bind ingredients like one whole egg. Two tablespoons of aquafaba is about the equivalent of one egg white. This is a great substitute for your favourite cakes and chocolate mousse recipes.
Don't believe us? Try our Liquid Gold Brownies recipe to put it to the test!

JACKFRUIT CURRY

Serves 2 people; Nut free

Curry lovers rejoice! Introducing a new star: the jackfruit. Raw jackfruit makes a standout substitute for meat-based dishes, absorbing all the rich flavours and spice of a traditional Indian curry.

1. Place a large pot on medium heat. Once hot, add the oil. Fry the ginger and onions on low to medium heat for about 5 minutes until soft.

2. Add the turmeric, chilli, coriander and cumin powders. Add the tomatoes and a little water and cook on low to medium heat until the tomatoes are very soft.

3. Blend the onion-tomato mixture with a hand blender.

4. Add the jackfruit and 150ml of water. Add salt to taste and cook well for about 12–14 minutes on low to medium heat.

5. Garnish with coriander leaves and serve with rice or warm naan (Indian bread).

1 tablespoon oil

1 large or 2 medium red onions, chopped

2 teaspoons ginger, grated

2 tomatoes, chopped

1 teaspoon turmeric powder

⅛ teaspoon chilli powder

1 ½ teaspoon coriander powder

1 teaspoon cumin powder

1 × 400g cans of young/ unripe jackfruit*, drained and rinsed (drained weight: 225g)

Salt, to taste

Coriander leaves to garnish

Unfortunately, it's difficult to find young jackfruit in more sustainable packaging. We hope this will change soon!

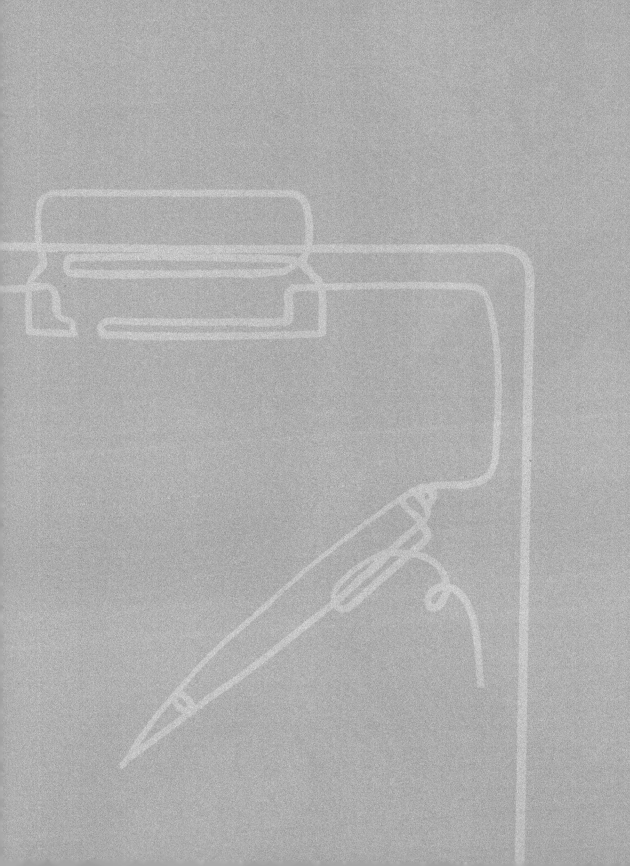

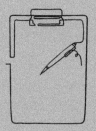

Be
PREPARED

"You must be the change you want to see in the world."
- Mahatma Gandhi

*P*lan ahead. It sounds like sensible advice, doesn't it? Yet, while we may plan ahead in other areas of our life, many of us don't when it comes to our meals. The reality is that when we don't have a plan for our meals, it's easy to fall back on food that is convenient and easy or just rely on the same old meals we've always cooked. Who needs yet another thing to think about, right?

What if we told you that with a little planning, easier and convenient can also be good for the planet and your health?

Planning ahead ensures that we stay on the path, in this case, the path to healthier and more sustainable eating habits. When we started planning meals ahead of time we found it saved time, stress, money and even minimised food waste. That's a win-win-win-win if you ask us. A little bit of preparation really does go a long way.

Plan Your Meals

*Y*ou might feel overwhelmed by the prospect of meal planning for plant-based meals or worry it will require too much effort. Trust us, it will get easier. As you get more comfortable with cooking plant-based dishes and discovering ingredients that work for you, it will become less daunting. When you start cooking plant-based dishes, make a note of:

- those that were quick to put together
- those that you enjoyed the most
- those that were comforting
- those that you would make when you had more time

It helps to have a few dishes on rotation every few weeks or even every week; practise definitely does make it easier. After a few weeks you should have a handful of plant-based dishes that you're comfortable putting together.

Keep it simple. Making a change is tough enough, driving yourself crazy trying to cook complex dishes with dozens of unfamiliar ingredients is a recipe for disaster, and for disappoint-ment. It's one of the reasons we are excited to share our recipes with you. They are the ones we cook for our own families on busy weeknights and lazy mornings. Simple, but delicious and healthy.

Breakfast is a great place to start. Making overnight oats, bircher muesli, chia pots or chia puddings the night before allows you to start your day with a healthy, no-fuss breakfast. Just top it off with some fruit, nuts and seeds and you're good to go. These breakfast ideas can be made quickly, even whilst your dinner is cooking. Whether you're eating at home or at work, it's one less thing to think about in the morning.

Thinking about your meals for the upcoming week is a great place to begin. This is a great weekend practise and it will set you up for the week. One of the greatest benefits of meal planning is shopping with a definitive list! Meal planning on the spot, while you're roaming the aisles, is hard. We often end up filling our shopping bags and trolleys with far more than we actually need, especially if we're lured by what's on offer. This is amplified when we go shopping on an empty stomach, when we're more prone to reach for food that will offer instant gratification, which often means highly processed products. Grocery shopping without a plan and with our stomachs rumbling is when we are most likely to be swayed by tempting marketing messages on packaging or to temporarily forget our long term goals of sustainable eating habits.

Batch Cooking

If you're busy like us, and who isn't these days, you may find batch cooking to be your biggest friend in planning meals. From pasta sauces to curries, cooking for more than one meal can come in handy when you're tight for time or to fill lunch boxes for work or school the next day. Some meals can even be frozen and taken out on a day when cooking a meal from scratch seems like too much of a chore. As you plan your meals for the week, think about one or two meals you can double up on. Use them the next day or pop them in the freezer for the future.

Vivienne & Poornima's Experience: We are Family

If the whole family isn't in the same place when it comes to eating more sustainably or even if there are a number of different food preferences, things can get challenging. We get it, because we have the same challenges in our own families. Though we are both 100% plant-based, our families aren't...yet! Sometimes this means that we supplement plant-based dishes with something non-plant based, other times the whole family enjoys fully plant-based meals.

We both have young children and our philosophy, especially with them, is never to force, but to have open conversations about the food we eat. We try, as best we can, to pass along the things we've learned and the experiences we've had with food and diet. As we spend time preparing and eating our meals, whether it's bean burgers on the BBQ or a traditional Indian dish, we talk to our families about foods and the different impact our food choices have on our bodies and the environment.

We hope that by helping our kids to understand why we make certain choices rather than just telling them, they will be better equipped to make their own choices.

Still, kids are kids. One of our children really can't stand the taste of plant-based yoghurt, and even though we're otherwise dairy-free, we still buy him Greek yoghurt to dollop on his favourite Indian dishes. Occasionally the kids will have a non plant-based ice-cream, but increasingly, the pleasure they get is quickly replaced by a stomach ache. They are becoming more and more conscious of the choices they make and how those choices affect their bodies.

It can take time, trial and error and a lot of patience to find the things that work for you and your family. It took a good deal of experimenting to find the perfect bean burger for the family barbeques we look forward to, but found it we did, and here's a secret: even though there will sometimes be meat for those who still occasionally eat it, everyone loves those bean burgers, even the meat-eaters!

Another tool we've both used with our families is the BBC's Climate Change Food Calculator used in our Make An Impact nudge. It's a really fun and engaging tool for the whole family, and a great visual and interactive exercise to bring the impact of our food choices to life in a very relatable way.

There are days when catering to a few different likes or dislikes can get tiring, or even frustrating – we're only human! – but mostly we're thrilled with the interest our families take in learning more about food, food choices, and how to eat for a better us.

There really is nothing more powerful than being a role model.

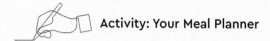 **Activity: Your Meal Planner**

Every week, plan for the week ahead. Depending on your goals, decide which meals will be plant-based and fill those in first. Use the recipes in this book to learn the basics of plant-based meal options. They may also inspire you to create your own recipes.

	Breakfast	Lunch	Dinner	Snacks
Monday				
Tuesday				
Wednesday				
Thursday				
Friday				
Saturday				
Sunday				

Kitchen Essentials

*J*ust as an artist or carpenter needs the right tools to do their best work, so do you. The list below isn't fancy, but it includes the right aids to help you make delicious, plant-based meals as easily as possible. Here are our kitchen essentials to get you started.

- Pots and pans of varying sizes
- Pressure cooker (optional)
- Spatulas and ladles
- Grater
- Garlic press
- Knives
- Chopping board
- Potato masher
- Mesh strainers of varying sizes
- Mixing bowls
- Deep and shallow baking trays
- Parchment/Baking paper
- Teaspoon and tablespoon measures
- Measuring jug in millilitres
- Weighing scale in grams
- Blender – hand or cup
- Full-size powerful blender
- Oven gloves
- Storage containers

What Do I Buy?

One of the most discouraging things about changing food habits can be figuring out what to buy, especially when some of the ingredients are not staples in our kitchen cupboards. Adding lots of new ingredients can be both time consuming – scouring supermarket aisles and health food stores – and expensive, so don't feel obliged to buy everything straight away.

The meal planning process will help you identify any new ingredients needed for recipes and you can add these to your weekly shopping list. This way you will only buy what you need, when you need it. If you have a zero-waste food store nearby, this also allows you to buy in the quantities that you need, saving you money and reducing the risk of food waste. It's also a great way to try out new ingredients without having to commit to large quantities.

Here is a list of common cupboard ingredients that you can keep handy to help you prepare plant-based meals. Simply add fresh produce, keeping it seasonal wherever possible, and you'll have everything you need to cook up a plant-based storm!

If you're struggling to find some of these ingredients, you can try online or start experimenting with those that are accessible to you.

Ingredients that I need to find alternatives for:

....
....
....
....
....

Breads, Tortillas & Whole Grain Flours

Choose breads that are 100% whole grain with little or no oil added. Enriched wheat flour, unbleached wheat flour, wheat flour, and organic wheat flour are not whole grain.

- Chickpea (gram) flour
- Oat flour
- Rice flour
- Rye bread
- Whole wheat flour
- Whole wheat bread
- Whole wheat tortillas

Dairy Alternatives

Choose unsweetened or minimally sweetened non-dairy milks. Avoid products with oils in the ingredient list.

- Coconut milk
- Coconut yoghurt
- Nut milks; almond, cashew, hazelnut
- Oat milk
- Plant-based butter
- Rice milk
- Soy milk

Ingredients to add to my shopping list:

....
....
....
....
....

Dried Fruits

Dried fruits are a good source of fibre and nutrients, but they should be eaten sparingly as they are a concentrated source of sugar. Look for options that don't have added sugar and try to avoid those with sulfites. Keep in mind they are higher in calories than fresh fruits and you don't get the benefit from the high water content of fresh fruits. We tend to avoid dried banana chips as many are actually fried.

- Apple
- Apricots
- Cranberries
- Dates
- Mango
- Raisins/sultanas

Dried Spices

- Basil
- Black pepper
- Cayenne pepper powder
- Chilli powder
- Cinnamon
- Coriander powder
- Cumin powder
- Garlic powder
- Ginger powder
- Italian seasoning
- Oregano
- Paprika
- Parsley
- Rosemary
- Thyme
- Turmeric powder

Ingredients to add to my shopping list:

....
....
....
....
....

Grains & Pasta

Check the ingredients list and choose whole grains as often as possible. For pastas, look for lentil or brown rice pasta.

- Barley
- Brown rice pasta
- Brown/white rice noodles
- Buckwheat noodles
- Bulgur
- Couscous
- Lentil pasta
- Millet
- Oats
- Quinoa
- Rice (basmati/jasmine/brown/wild)
- Whole durum wheat pasta

Legumes & Pulses: Plant-based Protein

Legumes and pulses are a great source of plant-based protein. To be sustainable, choose dry forms of these and boil them when needed. To save time, you can use packaged forms of some of these legumes and pulses; choose sustainable packaging whenever possible.

- Black beans
- Black eyed peas/beans
- Borlotti beans (rosecoco beans)
- Cannellini beans
- Kidney beans
- Pinto beans
- Tofu – firm (in chilled section)
- Tofu – silken
- White and brown chickpeas
- Yellow/red (orange) lentils

Ingredients to add to my shopping list:

....
....
....
....
....

Meat Substitutes

You might like to use these in some of your favourite meals if you want a meaty texture and flavour. As they can be highly processed, it's best to eat them occasionally.

- Jackfruit (a natural alternative with a meaty texture)
- Minced plant-based meat
- Plant-based burger patties
- Plant-based sausages

Nuts & Seeds

Look for the raw, unsalted versions without any added oils.

- Almonds
- Brazil nuts
- Cashews
- Chia seeds
- Ground flax seeds
- Hazelnuts
- Peanuts

- Pine nuts
- Pistachios
- Pumpkin seeds
- Sesame seeds
- Shelled hemp seeds
- Sunflower seeds
- Walnuts

Ingredients to add to my shopping list:

....
....
....
....
....

Oils

Use these sparingly for cooking and dressings.

- Coconut oil with neutral taste
- Olive oil
- Rapeseed oil
- Sesame oil
- Sunflower oil

Sauces, Dressings & Condiments

There are many options to boost the flavour of your food & dress your salads without adding any fat or sugar.

- Himalaya salt/rock salt/sea salt
- Kecap manis (sweet soy sauce)
- Mustard
- Nutritional yeast
- Tamari or soy sauce
- Vegetable stock cubes
- Vinegars: white, apple cider, balsamic, white balsamic, flavoured balsamic, white wine vinegar, unseasoned rice vinegar

Ingredients to add to my shopping list:

....
....
....
....
....

GRANOLA MUNCH

Makes one jar; Nut free

Nothing beats starting your day with homemade granola. Or munching it as a snack. Or... you get the picture. Bursting with goodness, it's simple to make "our" granola "yours" by adding your own favourites, like dried fruit, nuts, and seeds.

1. Preheat the oven to 180°C fan.

2. Put the jumbo oats, sunflower seeds and pumpkin seeds in a bowl. Give them a good mix.

3. Mix the coconut oil and maple syrup in a bowl and whisk together. Pour onto the oats and seeds and mix well so that they are evenly coated.

4. Pour the oat mixture onto a baking tray and spread evenly. Bake for 25 minutes, stirring a few times in between to avoid burning.

5. Add the coconut chips and desiccated coconut. Bake for a further 10 minutes, again stirring a few times to avoid burning.

6. Remove from the oven and let it cool completely so that it stays crunchy for longer.

7. Once cooled, add the raisins and give it a good mix. Store in an airtight container for a few weeks.

200g jumbo oats

25g sunflower seeds

25g pumpkin seeds

4 tablespoons melted coconut oil

3 tablespoons maple syrup

25g coconut chips

1 tablespoon desiccated coconut

50g raisins

SAVOURY PANCAKES

Serves 4 people; Nut free

If you're looking for a savoury breakfast option, then look no further. These golden pancakes are loaded with protein and greens and guaranteed to fire up your morning and set you up for the day ahead.

1. Add water to the chickpea flour in a large bowl and whisk well to remove lumps. Let it rest for about 15 minutes.

2. Whisk the chickpea-water batter again to remove as many lumps as possible. Small lumps are fine.

3. Add the onions, tomatoes, coriander leaves, cumin powder, chilli powder and salt. Whisk well.

4. Add the spinach and give it a good mix. Should the batter thicken, just add a little water to maintain the consistency of pancake batter.

5. Place a frying pan on medium heat. Once hot, add about ½ tablespoon of oil.

6. Pour about 3 tablespoons or a small ladle of batter onto the pan to make a round pancake. Cook on low to medium heat until golden on the underside. Flip to the other side and fry until golden, approximately 2 minutes per side.

7. You can keep the pancakes warm in a preheated oven at 120°C (fan setting) if needed.

8. Serve with ketchup.

9. Makes 12–14 of these golden circles of goodness.

300g chickpea flour (also known as gram flour)

400ml of water

1 small red onion, finely chopped

½ tomato, finely chopped

2 tablespoons coriander leaves, chopped

2 teaspoon ground cumin powder

¼ teaspoon chilli powder

40g baby spinach leaves, finely chopped or 6 cubes of frozen spinach, defrosted

Salt to taste

Oil

THE ORANGE SOUP

Serves 4 people; Nut free

Our favourite two-for-the-price-of-one soup. We love everything about this soup: the colour, the flavour, and just how many vegetables we can pack in. The best part? With one small step you can turn any leftovers into a delightfully creamy pasta sauce.

1. Preheat the oven to 200°C.

2. Place the tomatoes, sweet potatoes and carrots on a baking tray. Give it a good sprinkle of salt. Mix well.

3. Roast the vegetables for about 45 minutes until they are soft and tender.

4. Remove from the oven and cool.

5. Add tomatoes, sweet potato and carrots to a blender jar. Blend the vegetables into a very smooth texture.

6. Place on a pan to heat through before serving. Add water to adjust the consistency to your preference. Add salt and pepper to taste.

7. Serve with rye bread.

1kg tomatoes, cut into wedges

250–300g (2 medium) sweet potatoes, cut into 2cm chunks

300g carrots, chopped into chunks

Salt, to taste

Pepper, to taste

Handy Tip: You can use leftovers of the soup to make a creamy pasta sauce. Boil your favourite pasta as per the instructions. In a pan on medium heat place plant-based butter and allow it to melt. When it is almost fully melted, add a few ladles of the soup, depending on the quantity desired. Mix the butter and soup, add the pasta in and give it a good stir. Serve immediately.

BULGUR SALAD

Serves 4 people; Nut free

Parsley, lemon, and mint give this traditional Lebanese salad its distinctive, refreshing flavour, while bulgur adds the perfect amount of crunch. Our Tabbouleh makes a super lunch dish on its own, or served with our Roasted Red Bell Pepper and Cumin Hummus on the side. Add some warm pita and you've got a mini-mezze plate.

1. In a large bowl, mix together the bulgur, parsley, mint, lemon juice, olive oil, pomegranate seeds and apricots.

2. Add salt and pepper to taste. Mix well and serve.

135g bulgur, cooked as per package instructions

70g flat leaf parsley leaves, very finely chopped

10g mint leaves, very finely chopped

2 tablespoons lemon juice or the juice of ½ a lemon

1 tablespoon olive oil

3 tablespoons pomegranate seeds

4 apricots, chopped into small pieces (optional)

Salt, to taste

Pepper, to taste

PLANTIER'S PESTO

Makes a jar; Nut free

We love pesto, but it can be tricky to find a version that ticks our boxes and tickles our taste buds. Here's Plantier's recipe for a basil-based pesto which is both dairy and nut-free. Enjoy!

1. Put all the ingredients into a blender jar. Blend well until smooth (you will need a powerful blender to work through the seeds; we use the Nutribullet®).

2. Pour into a jar and enjoy with rye crackers, brown rice cakes, as a spread for sandwiches or to make a delicious bowl of creamy pesto pasta. Store in the fridge for 2–3 days.

100g fresh basil leaves (thin stems can be added), washed and drained

1 clove garlic, roughly chopped

4 tablespoons olive oil

1 tablespoon lemon juice

50g sunflower seeds

2 tablespoons water

½ teaspoon salt, or to taste

ALL-IN-A-JAR NOODLES

Serves 2 people; Nut free option

Noodles, assemble! This lunchtime staple definitely gives store-bought cup noodles a run for their money. A flash to put together, the ingredients can even be prepped the night before. When you're ready, add hot water, grab your chopsticks, and enjoy!

1. Pour the coconut milk into a small measuring jug. Add the curry, garlic and ginger powders and salt. Mix well with a fork or small whisk.

2. Pour the coconut milk mixture equally into 2 medium-sized glass mason jars.

3. Equally distribute and layer the cucumber, beetroot, baby spinach leaves, glass noodles, bean sprouts and enoki mushrooms between the jars.

4. Top each jar with spring onions, coriander leaves, peanuts, fried onions and red chilli. Squeeze a little lime juice into each jar. Cover.

5. When ready to eat, fill each jar with 200ml of boiling water. Cover and leave to rest for about 4 minutes or as per the package instructions of the glass noodles. Grab your chopsticks and enjoy.

165ml coconut milk

½ teaspoon store-bought curry powder

¼ teaspoon garlic powder

¼ teaspoon ginger powder

½ teaspoon salt, or to taste

85g cucumber, diced into small cubes

20g beetroot, julienned

14g baby spinach leaves

50g glass noodles, uncooked

20g bean sprouts

25g enoki mushrooms, with the ends chopped off

1 stalk spring onions, chopped

10g coriander leaves and thin stems

20g peanuts, crushed (optional)

2 teaspoons fried onions (optional)

½ red chilli, sliced (optional)

½ lime, sliced into 2 wedges

400ml boiling water

SPINACH DAL

Serves 4 people; Nut free

The humble dal. A staple in Indian households across the world, for many, the dish is synonymous with comfort and home. A wholesome treat packed full of protein, this one truly is a family favourite.

1. Place a pot or pressure cooker on medium heat. Once hot, add oil. Fry the onions and ginger on low to medium heat for approximately 5 minutes until they soften.

2. Add chopped tomatoes and cook on low to medium heat for about 5 minutes until soft. Add a little water if needed to prevent onions from burning.

3. Add turmeric, red chilli powder and coriander powders. Stir on low to medium heat. Add the spinach, lentils, water and salt. Stir well.

4. Pressure cook on low to medium heat for 6 minutes after the steam begins. If boiling, bring to a boil on medium heat. Reduce heat and simmer for about 10-12 minutes. You may need to add some water if boiling the lentils.

5. Garnish with coriander leaves.

6. Serve with white or brown rice.

1 teaspoon oil

1 teaspoon ginger, crushed

1 red onion, finely chopped

1 tomato, finely chopped

1 teaspoon turmeric powder

¼ teaspoon chilli powder

1 teaspoon coriander powder

60g fresh baby spinach, chopped or 4 cubes of chopped frozen spinach

150g yellow/red (orange) lentils, washed thoroughly

1.1L water

Salt to taste

Coriander leaves to garnish

Handy tip: You can use other types of lentils in this recipe depending on what's available in your kitchen cupboards or in the supermarket. Cooking times and water needed may vary if using other types of lentils. Add more water if needed when pressure cooking or boiling.

RED BELL PEPPER AND TOMATO PASTA

Serves 4 people; Nut free

Everyone knows the secret's in the sauce. And the secret to this sauce? It's a breeze to double up and freeze. Pour it over pasta, use it for lunches or pull out and defrost the next time you need a quick, homemade meal. Buon appetito!

1. Place a large pot on medium heat. Once hot, add the olive oil. Add the garlic and red bell pepper, fry on low to medium heat for 5 minutes until the red bell pepper is soft.

2. Add the tomato (passata), oregano and basil. Add salt. Cover and simmer on low to medium heat for 10 minutes.

3. Take off the heat and leave it to cool slightly. Use a hand blender and blend the pasta sauce until smooth.

4. Mix with your favourite pasta. Garnish with plant-based parmesan, if desired.

2 tablespoons olive oil

6 cloves garlic, crushed

1 red bell pepper, chopped

1.2L tomato sauce (passata)

1 tablespoon dried oregano

1 tablespoon dried basil

Salt, to taste

500g pasta, cooked as per package instructions

Plant-based parmesan cheese (optional)

HOME STYLE
BEAN CURRY WITH
CUMIN POTATOES

Serves 4 people; Nut free

A North Indian staple, this bean curry is a protein powerhouse that is worth the prep time. The scent of ginger, turmeric, and coriander will get your mouth watering and cumin potatoes add the perfect balance. To save time, see the handy tip. Enjoy with warm basmati rice.

Handy tip: To save time with pressure cooking or boiling the beans, you can use 300g of drained and washed canned borlotti/pinto/kidney beans or black eyed peas, and enjoy an even bigger variety of pulses in your meals. Remember to choose sustainable packaging whenever possible. In step 5 of the curry recipe above, add about 600ml of water instead and bring to a boil. Simmer for 10 minutes and continue with step 6.

Borlotti Beans Curry

1. Soak the beans overnight or for at least 6 hours in plenty of water. Rinse well and drain. Set aside.

2. Place a pot or pressure cooker on medium heat. Once hot, add the oil. Fry the onions, ginger and garlic on low to medium heat until onions are soft. This should take approximately 5–7 minutes.

3. Add the tomatoes and turmeric, coriander and chilli powders. Add a little water to bring it all together. Cook well for approximately 7 minutes until it turns very soft.

4. Use a hand blender to blend the onion and tomato mixture.

5. Add the beans and 1L of water. Pressure cook on medium heat for 45–50 minutes after the steam begins. If boiling, bring to a boil on medium heat. Reduce heat and simmer for about 60–75 minutes, until the beans are very soft. You may need to add some more water if boiling the beans.

6. Mash some of the beans with a potato masher to thicken the curry.

7. Garnish with coriander leaves and serve with basmati rice.

1 tablespoon oil

2 big red onions, chopped

2 teaspoons ginger, peeled and grated

3 cloves garlic, crushed

3 tomatoes, chopped

1 teaspoon turmeric powder

2 teaspoons coriander powder

¼ teaspoon chilli powder

300g borlotti beans (also known as rosecoco beans)

Salt, to taste

1L water

Few coriander leaves, roughly chopped

Cumin Potatoes

1. Place a frying pan on medium heat. Once hot, add the oil. Add the cumin seeds and fry for about half a minute until they start popping.

2. Lower the heat. Add the turmeric and chilli powders, and fry for about half a minute.

3. Add a little water and then the potatoes and green bell pepper. Stir well so the potatoes and green peppers are evenly coated with the spices.

4. Add salt, cover and let it cook on low to medium heat, stirring occasionally. Add a little more water if necessary. Too much water will cause the potatoes to become too soft so add water only as needed.

5. When the potatoes are almost cooked, remove the cover and let the water evaporate while lightly browning the potatoes.

6. Serve as a side dish to the borlotti beans curry and rice.

1 tablespoon oil

1 tablespoon cumin seeds

1 teaspoon turmeric powder

¼ teaspoon chilli powder

1kg potatoes, peeled and cut into 2cm cubes

1 green bell pepper, cut into 2cm cubes

Salt, to taste

HEALTHIER-THAN-TAKE-OUT UDON NOODLES

Serves 4 people; Nut free

What if we told you that you could have the taste of take-out, but better for your body? These udon noodles might just make you toss your takeaway menus in the bin.

1. Place a frying pan on medium heat. Once hot, add 1 tablespoon of sesame oil. Fry the tofu on low to medium heat until light brown. Set aside.

2. Mix rice vinegar, tamari and maple syrup in a bowl and keep aside.

3. Place the frying pan back on medium heat. Once hot, add 1 tablespoon of sesame oil. Fry the onions, ginger, garlic and fresh red chilli on low to medium heat for about 5 minutes until the onions are soft.

4. Add the light green part of the spring onions and fry on low to medium heat for 1 minute.

5. Add the mixed vegetables and cook on medium heat until they just begin to soften. Add bean sprouts. Cook for 3-4 minutes, careful not to overcook the vegetables.

6. Add noodles, sauce mixture and toss well. Add salt if needed.

7. Serve garnished with the rest of the spring onions.

2 tablespoons sesame oil

500g firm tofu, cut into 1cm cubes

2 teaspoons rice vinegar

4 tablespoons tamari/soy sauce

1 teaspoon maple syrup

1 medium red onion, sliced

2 tablespoons ginger, julienned

3 cloves garlic, chopped

1 fresh red chilli, finely chopped

2 stalks spring onions, chopped (optional)

200g mixed vegetables, chopped (we use carrots and cabbage)

200g bean sprouts

300g udon noodles, cooked as per package instructions

Salt, to taste

BROWN CHICKPEAS PULAO

Serves 4 people; Nut free

Another traditional Indian dish that makes the perfect one-pot meal. Flavoured by spices, powered by plant-based protein, this pulao is perfection. Serve with raita, a yoghurt dressing.

Pulao

1. Place a large pot over medium heat. Once hot, add the oil. Fry the onions, garlic and ginger on low to medium heat for about 5 minutes until onions are soft, stirring frequently.

2. Add the dry spice powders and spices and stir on low to medium heat for approximately 1 minute.

3. Add the tomatoes. Fry on low to medium heat until the tomatoes are soft, then add the brown chickpeas and garam masala. Let it cook for 5–7 minutes.

4. Add the basmati rice, water and salt. Stir well, cover and bring to the boil on medium heat. Once the water begins to boil, reduce the heat to low and simmer until the water is fully absorbed and rice is cooked through, about 20 minutes. Stir occasionally to avoid the rice at the bottom from burning.

5. Serve hot with raita on the side.

1 tablespoon oil

2 medium red onions, sliced

2 cloves garlic, crushed

1 teaspoon ginger, grated

½ teaspoon turmeric powder

⅛ teaspoon chilli powder

1 teaspoon cumin seeds

2 bay leaves

2 black cardamom pods (optional)

1 star anise

3–4 cloves

3 tomatoes, chopped

240g cooked brown chickpeas

½ teaspoon garam masala*

450g basmati rice

600ml water

3–4 teaspoons salt (depending on preference)

Yoghurt Dressing

1. Place the yoghurt in a bowl. Add salt, cumin and chilli powders and whisk.

2. Serve with the pulao as an accompaniment.

300g natural, unsweetened soy or coconut yoghurt

1 teaspoon salt

½ teaspoon cumin powder

Pinch of chilli powder

Have

YOUR CAKE

"Nothing in life is to be feared. It is only to be understood."
- Marie Curie

80/20 Eating

Though we often lose sight of it, the fact is, food is meant to be enjoyed. It is fuel for our bodies and minds, but it is more than that. It's pleasure and comfort and a way we connect. Our relationship with food shouldn't be about being virtuous or overly restrictive. We all have birthdays, holidays, celebrations and weekends. When it comes to small food indulgences, we believe that the frequency with which we consume them is key.

The 80/20 rule is a valuable mindset to help us approach our food and diets in a healthy and sustainable way, especially if we are hoping to navigate change. The premise is simple: 80% of the time eat and drink well. Ideally this would mean minimally processed, whole foods used to make home cooked meals. During the remaining 20% of the time, give yourself the freedom to enjoy foods that perhaps aren't as healthy. For some that might mean a sweet treat, for others it might be something savoury. If we're confident that the majority of time we are feeding our minds and bodies with health-giving, whole foods, when it comes to those moments of celebration and socialising, we can relax a little bit and really relish our food. Feeling in control means empowerment.

When we are making changes to our lives, we need to be kind, patient and forgiving of ourselves. Remember that every time you take action towards your goals, however small or large, you're moving forward. Keep the focus on progress over perfection.

If you've made the choice to transition to a more plant-based diet, or even if you're dipping a toe in the water, it might feel like some of your favourite food indulgences are off limits. The combination of the crowding-out method outlined in our *Take Your Time* nudge and the 80/20 mindset will help support these changes at a pace and in a way that works for you.

Poornima's Experience: Holding on to the Buratta

During my transition to a fully plant-based diet, I had one main weakness and that was for burrata! Generally I have good self-control, but this creamy cheese really challenged me. In some ways, I was lucky it wasn't something that I consumed on a daily basis, it was really only when we ate at Italian restaurants. The problem was that consuming it – even occasionally – left me with stomach issues that lasted days and sometimes even weeks as it wreaked havoc on my energy and well-being. The first step was overcoming my denial. How could the cheese I relished be the problem? Once I acknowledged that it was, the trick was to consciously remind myself of the way it made me feel. It wasn't easy to give it up and it took some immense self-control not to nibble whenever we ate out, but today, I am thankful for it. And my body thanks me too. Over time, my desire for indulging in burrata has certainly reduced. In the case of burrata, the percentages were reversed: 20% of the satisfaction I got wasn't worth 80% of the indigestion.

Beware the *Bliss Point*

What is the bliss point and why are we advising you to be wary of it? The *bliss point* is defined as "a name given in food manufacturing to the amount of sugar, salt and fat that makes a product taste as good as possible".[117] Food companies use this principle to make their foods irresistible, which keeps us coming back for more. With the meteoric rise in vegan and plant-based foods it's important to keep these new products in mind; just because they are marketed as "healthy" does not mean they are exempt from this magic product formulation.

Many products are profiting from the halo-effect of traditionally healthy vegan labels. Even the term 'plant-based' has taken on a new meaning, from its original intention of whole foods to something that does not contain animal products. Labels can be misleading, and we encourage you to read them carefully. There's no need to avoid these foods completely, and we certainly enjoy them on occasion, but being conscious of what we're putting into our bodies is key.

A Spoonful of Sugar

Over time, the bliss point has really thrown our taste buds out of whack and most of us have become accustomed to overly sweet and sugary foods. Refined sugar is found in all the places you'd expect to find it – soft drinks, cakes, biscuits and pastries, but also lurks in sauces, dressings, yoghurts and other savoury processed foods. Eating these foods makes our blood sugar levels spike, and because the body processes them so quickly, we're left feeling hungry, and the cycle perpetuates. By eating whole foods 80% of the time, you will reduce much of your 'hidden' sugar intake. A benefit? You will really appreciate and savour the sugar you choose.

The great news is that there are healthier ways to indulge a sweet tooth. Dried fruit provides both the sweetness and sticky texture you need to make some truly decadent treats. Using fruit to sweeten dishes also means that we are getting more fibre, which helps us to feel fuller. That's why many plant-based desserts and treats are made with dates and ripe bananas.

Unrefined sugars, also known as natural sweeteners, are frequently used too. Products like coconut sugar, maple syrup and molasses feature in recipes and packaged goods. Whilst the name 'natural' suggests they are on par with the health benefits of fruit, in reality, they have the same impact on our bodies as refined sugars. Although they may have slightly more nutrients, they should still be eaten in moderation.

Eggs-cellent Alternatives

Baking without dairy and eggs felt a little daunting at first, but we were amazed at just how many egg alternatives are out there. Substitutes or replacements are not one-size-fits-all, however, and they might behave differently depending on the other ingredients in your recipe. Some of the replacements may surprise you:

- Flax eggs – made with ground flax seeds and water.

- Chia eggs – made with chia seeds and water.

- Aquafaba – we said there may be some surprises, and this is definitely one of them! Sometimes referred to as 'liquid gold', aquafaba is the liquid found in a tin of chickpeas, or the water they have been soaking in if you're preparing them from dried. When whisked, it resembles the fluffy white peaks of egg whites.

- Mashed or pureed fruits – apple sauce, mashed ripe bananas and pumpkin puree often feature because of their binding nature, they also help to bring a natural sweetness.

- Apple cider vinegar and baking soda – another unusual option reminiscent of a science experiment! We've used this combination in several cake recipes with good results.

When using alternatives for baking, it isn't as simple as replacing like for like. Generally, we like to stick to tried and tested recipes in cookbooks or online as they have done all the hard work perfecting the optimum taste and texture.

From a savoury standpoint, we've found that tofu, silken and firm, is a successful alternative to eggs. Tofu scramble makes for a delicious breakfast, brunch or lunch option and is a great plant-based source of protein. Adding turmeric provides the yellow colouring of scrambled egg and seasoning helps to spice things up.

Chewing the Fat

In our *Cultivate Your Health* nudge, we discussed 'good' and 'bad' fats with or without animal produce. When it comes to baking, two of our favourite fats are plant-based butter and coconut oil. Again, choosing which to use depends a lot on other ingredients, especially from a flavour and texture perspective. Coconut oil gives a smooth texture and offers a hint of coconutty flavour and scent. It usually needs to be melted before using, which is one of the key differences compared to plant-based butter, which can be incorporated as is.

With savoury dishes, and depending on the cuisine, vegetable or seed oils can be transformative. Sesame oil is delicious in Asian-inspired dishes, and olive oil in Meditteranean-inspired meals. They also make the perfect base for salad dressings and sauces, which add flavour and appeal to vegetables, both hot and cold.

Going Loco for Cocoa

What's a section about treating yourself without talking about chocolate? Dark chocolate is one of our favourite ways to indulge. When we first eliminated dairy, we assumed that all dark chocolate was dairy free, but we quickly discovered that wasn't the case. Generally, plain chocolate bars are dairy free, but those with centres like caramel, praline and coconut more often than not contain milk. Even dark chocolate bars with a hint of flavour like sea salt, orange, mint or chilli can include milk in the form of butter fat, which is used to create a softer texture and extend the shelf life. Another reason to quickly scan the back of the packet to make sure you know what you're eating!

It's not *all* about chocolate though, there are many other ways to enjoy cacao. There might be some confusion between the terms 'cacao' and 'cocoa', and the two are sometimes used interchangeably. Generally, cacao refers to products that haven't been heavily processed and are in their more natural form, like cacao nibs, cacao butter and raw cacao powder. Cocoa, in the form of cocoa powder, has been processed through high temperatures. Cocoa powder is the one we often find on supermarket shelves and it can, but not always, include refined sugar. We love to use unsweetened cocoa powder or raw cacao powder to make our own hot chocolate. The combination of plant milk, maple syrup and cocoa powder makes a creamy, intensely chocolatey treat. For a crunchier texture and more bitter flavour, cacao nibs are another way to enjoy a chocolatey hit. Sprinkled on breakfast, mixed in with some nuts, used as a dessert topping or as an alternative to chocolate chips, they are a great way to satisfy your chocolate cravings without the added sugar.

There is a bitter note to our chocolate consumption. Modern slavery and child labour practices in the chocolate industry are long over-due isues to address and shine a light upon. [118] Organisations like Fairtrade[119] are helping to bring some parity back to the chocolate industry, providing farmers with fair pay and for some, the ability to invest in their community. You might like to explore your favourite chocolate brand to see where and how they source their chocolate.

Vivienne's Experience: Choc-a-Block

It probably doesn't come as a surprise that I have a sweet tooth and love chocolate! Milk chocolate was my absolute favourite and I have fond memories of it. My grandparents would always bring a big bar to share when they came to visit, and it came in 'selection boxes' at Christmas and foil-wrapped eggs for Easter. I guess I associated chocolate with celebrations and spending time with my family.

For many years I read about the benefits of dark chocolate, and knew to choose bars with higher cocoa solids and to have just a little at a time. However, after years of eating very sweet and milky chocolate, dark chocolate wasn't tickling my taste buds in the same way. Even after I received my test results, which confirmed just how intolerant I am to dairy, I still couldn't resist. In fact, it took me almost two years after these results to stop eating it. Although I wasn't aware at the time, I was naturally using the 'crowding out' principle by slowly switching from milk to dark chocolate. It took some time, but as it turns out, all the articles were right, without the added 'bliss-point' ingredients, over time the natural intensity of dark chocolate satisfied my sweet tooth and I wanted less of it.

EASY CACAO
OVERNIGHT OATS

Serves 2 people; Nut free

A sweet treat of a breakfast you can make the night before. Super simple, super tasty. What could be better?

1. Mix the oats, cacao powder, and dates/raisins in a bowl. Soak this mixture in the non-dairy milk. Cover and let it sit in the fridge for at least an hour or overnight.

2. Before eating, mix with the additional non-dairy milk and coconut sugar.

3. Divide between bowls and top with sliced bananas, berries and coconut flakes.

115g rolled oats

250ml unsweetened non-dairy milk

1 tablespoon cacao powder

2 pitted dates, chopped or 10 jumbo raisins

Additional 125ml unsweetened non-dairy milk

1 ½ teaspoons of coconut sugar

½ a large banana, sliced

Fresh berries

Dehydrated coconut flakes

"FAUXGHURT" SMOOTHIE BOWL

Serves 1 person; Nut free option

Fresh berries and avocado blended together to create a creamy fruit "yoghurt". Add seeds and nuts to create your own nutrient powerhouse.

1. Put the frozen berries, avocado, ground flax seeds, chia seeds, nut butter and plant milk into a blender cup.

2. Blend until the colour is even and the texture is smooth.

3. Pour into a bowl and top with seeds. If you're taking it out on the go with you, keep it in the blender cup, top with the pumpkin and shelled hemp seeds and pop the lid on to keep it fresh for when you're ready to enjoy it.

Handful of frozen blueberries

Half a small avocado

2 tablespoons ground flax seeds

1 tablespoon chia seeds

1 tablespoon nut butter (exclude for nut-free version)

150ml plant milk

Toppings

Pumpkin seeds

Shelled hemp seeds

Handy tip: To vary the flavour and the nutrients of your smoothie bowl, use different frozen berries and seeds.

HOT CHOCOLATE

Serves 1 person; Nut free

Nothing beats wrapping your hands around a mug of hot chocolate on a cool day. Dial up the decadence by adding a scoop of plant-based ice-cream.

1. Put the oat milk, cacao/cocoa powder and raw sugar in a small saucepan on medium heat and whisk.

2. Bring it to a boil on medium heat. Lower the heat and simmer for 1 minute. Pour into a mug ready to drink. Add the ice cream if desired.

240ml oat milk

1 ½ teaspoons cacao/unsweetened cocoa powder

½ teaspoon sugar/raw sugar/brown sugar

1 scoop of plant-based vanilla ice cream (optional)

R'S VANILLA-CHOCO SHAKE

Serves 1–2 people; Nut free option

It might get messy, but we love it when the kids get creative in the kitchen. A vanilla milkshake with just a hint of chocolate for those days when you can't decide between the two!

1. Add the oat milk, ice-cream and cacao/cocoa powder to a blender jar.

2. Blend for about 30 seconds until smooth.

3. Pour into two small glasses. Top with a dusting of cacao/cocoa powder.

200ml oat milk

3 scoops of plant-based vanilla ice-cream

1 teaspoon cacao/unsweetened cocoa powder

Extra cacao/unsweetened cocoa powder for dusting

CHOCOLATE CHIP COOKIES

Makes 24 cookies; Nut free option

Sometimes you just need a cookie. When the craving strikes, try these chocolate chip treats, made with spelt flour, muscovado sugar, and dark chocolate chips. We love to make a batch and freeze half for another day.

1. Preheat the oven to 180°C; line 2 baking trays with reusable baking sheets.

2. Beat the plant-based butter, sugar, vanilla extract and maple syrup with an electric cake mixer in a bowl until creamy.

3. Add the flour, baking powder and salt. Beat again until well combined.

4. Add the dark chocolate chips and use a wooden spoon to fold them in.

5. Use your hands to shape balls (about 1 heaped tablespoon) of the cookie dough. They spread out a fair bit so leave adequate space between them on the baking tray. Place on the baking tray and flatten slightly with your fingers or the back of a fork.

6. Put the baking trays, one at a time, in the oven for about 12–14 minutes until golden brown. Cool down on the tray for 5–10 minutes and then transfer to a wire rack for further cooling.

250g plant-based butter (some plant-based butter have almonds in them so look out for nut free options to make these cookies nut free)

220g muscovado sugar

2 teaspoons vanilla extract

1 tablespoon maple syrup

300g spelt flour

1 teaspoon baking powder

½ teaspoon salt

100g dark chocolate chips

RASPBERRY COMPOTE

Makes one jar; Nut free

When your breakfast or dessert is screaming out for a little something extra, this simple berry compote is going to be your new best friend. It's never been easier to add a pop of colour, a swirl of sweetness, and an extra helping of fruit and seeds to your day.

1. Place a small saucepan on medium heat. Add the berries, chia seeds and water. Cook for 5 minutes, allowing time for the berries to defrost. Using a spatula, separate out the fruit by cutting into the clusters of berries and then stir to combine all the ingredients.

2. Turn up the heat slightly to medium to high heat for another 10 minutes, stirring frequently to avoid the fruit or seeds sticking to the bottom of the pan. The fruit will break down and it should have the consistency of runny jam.

3. You can either enjoy it hot straight from the pan, or to use at another time, pour the mixture into a glass jar. Allow it to cool before sealing with a lid, and store in the fridge for up to 2 weeks.

350g frozen raspberries

2 tablespoons chia seeds

100ml water

Handy tip: You can change this recipe to include any frozen berries or combine a few together. Making a fruit compote is a great way to fight food waste and use up fresh berries that are past their best. You can either pop them straight in the pan (we would recommend adding the water slowly as fresh berries tend to use less water in this recipe) or rinse them and freeze them to use another time.

ORCHARD FRUIT OATY BARS

Makes 16 squares; Nut free

A naturally sweet treat that pulls its flavour from dried apricots and raisins, these oaty squares are a favourite lunch box treat, and not just for the kids!

1. Preheat the oven to 180°C (fan).

2. Put the dried apricots in a heat resistant bowl and cover with boiling water for 10 minutes, to rehydrate and soften.

3. In a large mixing bowl, mix together the oats and raisins.

4. When the apricots are ready, use a spoon to transfer them to a blender jar. Then add the maple syrup and melted coconut oil along with 125ml of the water the apricots have been soaking in. Blend into a smooth, thick paste.

5. Pour the apricot mixture into the mixing bowl with the oats and raisins. Mix well until all the oats are covered. It is really important to make sure they are all covered as the oats absorb the mixture and soften whilst in the oven.

6. Transfer the mixture into a parchment/baking paper lined square cake tin (approximately 21cmx21cm), and spread evenly.

7. Bake for about 20–25 minutes or until it starts to brown at the edges.

8. Remove from the oven and leave to cool for 5 minutes, before lifting by the parchment/baking paper and cooling on a rack. Cut into 16 squares and enjoy.

250g dried apricots

250g rolled oats (option to use gluten free oats)

100g raisins

4 tablespoons coconut oil, melted

3 tablespoons maple syrup

125ml water, reserved from soaking the apricots

SWEET SQUARES

Makes 16 squares; Nut free

When the aroma of simmering coconut sugar fills our kitchens, everyone knows what's coming. A pinch of cardamom gives an unexpected boost to these sweet treats.

1. Place a saucepan on medium heat. Once hot, add oil and plant-based butter. Heat until butter is melted. Reduce heat to low and add the semolina.

2. Cook on low heat until the semolina changes colour slightly (to a very pale brown). Ensure you do this on low heat so as to not burn the semolina. You may need to be a little patient here as this may take up to 10 minutes, but trust us, the patience pays off. Take it off the heat and set aside.

3. Put the sugar and water in a saucepan on medium to high heat. Stir occasionally and bring to the boil. Reduce the heat to low and simmer for 7–8 minutes.

4. When the sugar water is ready, put the pan with the semolina back onto low heat and add the sugar water one ladle at a time. Be careful of splashes. Once you have added all the sugar water, add the cardamom powder and use the back of a spatula to smooth the mixture so that there are no lumps. Stir until the mixture thickens and starts to pull away from the side of the pan. This should only take a minute or two.

5. Transfer to a square cake tin (approximately 21cmx-21cm), or any heatproof dish of the same size, greased with a little oil. Once cool, cut into squares and enjoy.

1 tablespoon plant-based butter

1 tablespoon oil plus a little extra to grease the square tin

135g semolina

75g coconut sugar

600ml water

½ teaspoon cardamom powder

COCONUT CHIA PUDDING

Serves 2-4 people; Nut free

Cuckoo for coconut? This unfussy dessert can be made ahead of time and is an all-time winner in our homes.

1. Whisk coconut milk and chia seeds until smooth in a bowl.

2. Pour into 4 small bowls or ramekins.

3. Place the bowls or ramekins in the fridge for at least 4 hours.

4. Before serving, drizzle the maple syrup and top with coconut flakes and berries or chopped mango.

400ml coconut milk*

2 tablespoons chia seeds

Maple syrup to drizzle

Coconut flakes for garnish

Berries or chopped mango

* You can use light coconut milk to keep it lighter as a breakfast treat. If doing so, increase the amount of chia seeds to 3 tablespoons to ensure it sets well.

CHOCOLATE DIVINE CAKE

Makes 12 servings or 24 cupcakes; Nut free option

There is something undeniably divine about chocolate cake, like a little slice of heaven. Dark chocolate chips add to the richness of this decadent treat and vanilla icing brings it to a whole new level of indulgence.

Chocolate Cake

1. Preheat the oven to 180°C.

2. In a medium-sized mixing bowl, add the dry ingredients; plain flour, cacao/cocoa powder, raw sugar, baking soda and table salt. Mix well with a wooden spoon until evenly combined.

3. Make three wells in the dry ingredients with a large spoon. Add the white vinegar, vanilla extract and vegetable oil into each of the three wells.

4. Pour in the water and mix well with a whisk until all the ingredients are well combined, approximately 1 minute.

5. Stir in the dark chocolate chips with a large spoon.

6. Pour into a greased and floured square cake tin (approximately 21cmx21cm). Bake for 35 minutes. Alternatively, line 2 cupcake trays with cupcake liners. Pour the cake batter into each so that it is about half full. Bake for 20 minutes.

225g plain flour

3 tablespoons cacao/unsweetened cocoa powder

240g raw sugar

1 teaspoon baking soda

½ teaspoon table salt

1 teaspoon white vinegar

1 teaspoon vanilla extract

5 tablespoons vegetable oil plus a little extra to grease the square tin

250ml water

100g dark chocolate chips

7. To test if your cake is cooked, insert a clean wooden skewer into the centre of the cake and remove it. With the addition of the dark chocolate chips that would have melted, you may need to test in a few places. If the cake is cooked, the skewer will come out clean. If not, pop it back into the oven for a few extra minutes.

8. Remove from the oven and leave to cool completely before transferring onto a cake board, ready to be enjoyed. You may want to add some of our vanilla or chocolate icing on top to make for an extra decadent treat.

Vanilla Icing

1. In a medium-sized mixing bowl, beat the plant-based butter, powdered sugar, vanilla extract and oat milk with an electric cake mixer until creamy, approximately 1 – 1 ½ minutes.

2. Store in the fridge until ready to ice the cake. You can use a spatula to spread this icing on the cake or use it in a piping bag to decorate the cake. Add a few drops of oat milk and beat to adjust the consistency to what you need.

3. Option 1 and 2: You can add a few drops of your favourite food colouring for a splash of colour or add cacao/unsweetened cocoa powder. Mix well. Spread or pipe and enjoy!

100g plant-based butter (some plant-based butter have almonds in them so look out for nut free options to make the icing nut free)

500g icing or powdered sugar

1 ½ teaspoons vanilla extract

3 tablespoons of oat milk

Additional icing options:

Colourful icing: Add a few drops of food colouring; you could even divide the icing into portions and add different colours of food colouring to each portion.

Chocolate icing: Add 30g of cacao/unsweetened cocoa powder and 1 tablespoon of oat milk to the basic vanilla icing recipe for even more of a chocolatey treat.

LIQUID GOLD BROWNIES

Makes 16 squares; Nut free option

*Sssh.. our brownie delights have a secret. This classic family favourite uses 'liquid gold'
- aquafaba – as an eggs-cellent substitute. Served on their own or with a scoop of plant-
based vanilla ice cream, you'll go nuts for these gooey, chocolate treats.*

1. Preheat the oven to 180°C.

2. In a medium-sized mixing bowl, add the plant-based butter and raw sugar. Beat with an electric cake mixer until creamy, approximately 1 - 1 ½ minutes.

3. Add the aquafaba and beat for approximately 1 minute until combined.

4. Add the spelt flour, salt, baking powder and cacao/cocoa powder. Beat until very well combined, approximately 30 seconds.

5. Stir in the walnuts (if using) with a large spoon. If omitting, skip to step 6.

6. Transfer the mixture into a parchment/baking paper lined square cake tin (approximately 21cmx21cm), and spread evenly. You may need to use your hand to do this as it may stick to the spoon.

100g plant-based butter (some plant-based butter have almonds in them so look out for nut free options to make these brownies nut free)

230g raw sugar

6 tablespoons aquafaba (this is the liquid from a chickpea can or package; drain the chickpeas and save this liquid gold)

135g spelt flour

½ teaspoon table salt

1 ½ teaspoons baking powder

60g cacao/unsweetened cocoa powder

30g walnuts, chopped (optional)

7. Bake for 35–40 minutes. To test if your brownies are cooked, insert a clean wooden skewer into the centre of the brownies and remove it. If the brownies are ready, the skewer will come out fairly clean but with batter on it. If not, pop it back into the oven for a few extra minutes.

8. Place the pan on a wire rack and cool for five minutes. Then, grasping the edge of the parchment/baking paper, transfer the brownies onto the wire rack. Let them cool for at least another five minutes and then transfer onto a cutting board for slicing into 16 squares.

9. Serve on its own or with a scoop of vanilla ice cream.

Our Final Note

FROM US TO YOU

The old saying is true, we really *are* what we eat. But *what* we eat is so much more than just the forkfuls we put into our mouths. Our food habits are linked to our lifestyle, culture and identity and they play a huge role in our social engagements. Our relationship with food is intensely personal and yet, at the same time, those choices also have a deep impact on the planet we share. Our food habits today are not the same as those of our ancestors, just as those of our grandchildren will not be the same as ours today. The evidence supporting the move towards plant-based meals is growing. Whether you're eager to simply incorporate more plant-based meals into your lifestyle or go all-in, it's clear: we must all do more – for the health of our planet and our bodies.

At the same time, we know firsthand just how difficult it is to change food habits, or even to just think about making a change. It can seem overwhelming, scary or even not worth it. We also understand how confusing the information out there can seem. But we *also* believe that the desire to do better is within us all and that sometimes we just need a nudge or two ... or five. Throughout this book, we have used the idea of nudges, or gentle pushes, to help you along. In each of our five nudges, we have distilled the information out there into bite-sized nuggets, hopefully making it easier for you to chew on, while also providing you with practical tools and tips. It's our hope that these nudges will help you gradually embed more plant-based meals into your daily and weekly food habits.

Whether your reasons are personal, planetary, or both, we encourage you to think about the bigger picture. Focus on small, manageable changes that you can make. Remember that every, single plant-based meal adds to a better you and a better planet. Whatever you decide, remember that this is your personal journey. Be bold; Be confident; Be unapologetic about your choices.

When each of us took our first steps towards a more sustainable diet of plant-based foods, we were very much on our own. That's the last thing we want for you. We know that if you want to, you can make the change. On the last few pages we're leaving you with a set of simple, clear actions for each of the five nudges.

Empower yourself; One step at a time; We are here with you.

Welcome on this journey to a new, more sustainable you. Your body and your planet are already saying thank you.

Vivienne & Poornima

 **Get Nudged**

Make An Impact

- Keep a few facts handy like the 3000 L of water it takes to produce a single beef burger patty in comparison with 1,905 L of water needed to produce 150g of beans. This can help remind us of why we are on this journey.
- Play around with the BBC Climate Change Food Calculator with foods in your weekly diet.
- Do the Activity: How gassy are you?
- Watch *Cowspiracy*, *Forks over Knives*, and *A Life on Our Planet*.
- Cook an ingredient you use regularly in a different way.

Cultivate Your Health

- Do the Activity: 30-a-week tracker.
- Switch from refined grains to whole grains.
- Try a new plant food; fruit, vegetable, grain, pulse, nut, seed, herb or spice.
- If you have one nearby, visit your local farmer's market to find out what is in season and how they grow their produce.
- Watch *The Game Changers* and *What the Health*.

Take Your Time

- Understand the differences between being plant-based, flexitarian, vegetarian and vegan.
- Choose one meal to be plant-based: Remember that one plant-based meal a day for a year will save 736,895 litres of water and 350 kilograms of carbon emissions.
- Do the Activity: Your step-by-step guide to going plant-based.
- Swap an ingredient with a plant-based one.
- Ask for a plant-based dish when dining out.

Be Prepared

- Remind yourself that being prepared helps ensure that you are in control.
- Do the Activity: Your meal planner.
- Ensure you have all the kitchen essentials.
- Stock your pantry with plant-based groceries to make it easier for you.
- Make a big batch of one of our recipes and save it for lunch the next day.

Have Your Cake

- Remember the 80/20 rule; don't deny yourself.
- Be aware of the sugar in treats and seek alternatives.
- Sweeten your food with fresh, dried or frozen fruits.
- Switch to dark chocolate with a minimum of 70% cocoa solids.
- Try your hand at making a plant-based treat.

Resources to

INSPIRE YOU

FOOD DIARY

To help you get closer to what you're currently eating, you might like to try filling in a food diary. It can help identify patterns of what and how frequently you're consuming a particular food, as well as how it makes you feel both physically and emotionally. Did the 'How Gassy Are You?' activity at the start of the book highlight some foods that you would like to eat less or more of? Awareness is the first step to us wanting to change our habits.

Writing things down is a great way for us to be more conscious of what we're doing, whether it's keeping a food diary or journalling about life in general. It doesn't need to be done everyday. Try filling it in for three days, one of which should be a weekend day as they tend to be a little more freestyle. What patterns do you spot?

- Where are there opportunities to add in more plant-based foods in your meal or snack times?
- What would be the easiest change to make?
- Do you tend to stick to the same foods or do you mix it up?
- Are there some foods/meals that give you more or less energy or concentration?
- Are there some foods/meals that make you feel bloated or uncomfortable?

Activity: My Food Diary

What I ate for...	How are you feeling physically?	How are you feeling emotionally?
Breakfast		
Lunch		
Dinner		
Snacks		

How many different types of the following did you consume today?

Fruits	Pulses
Vegetables	Nuts & Seeds
Grains	Herbs & Spices

COOKBOOKS

These are the cookbooks we always have to hand. All plant-based, they cover everything from clean eating to more indulgent, comfort food, and we have loved exploring the recipes.

- *Bosh* by Henry Firth and Ian Theasby
- *Bish Bash Bosh* by Henry Firth and Ian Theasby
- *Deliciously Ella – The Plant-Based Cookbook* by Ella Mills
- *Thug Kitchen – The Official Cookbook*
- *The Doctor's Kitchen* by Dr. Rupy Aujla
- *The Clean Plate* by Gwyneth Paltrow
- *Eat Clean Play Dirty* by Danielle Duboise and Whitney Tingle
- *Green Kitchen Stories* by Luise Vindahl and David Frenkiel
- *My New Roots* by Sara Britton
- *Power Bowls* by Kate Turner
- *The Modern Cook's Year* by Anna Jones

NUTRITION & PLANT-BASED BOOKS

We have been so inspired by these books, and they have really shaped our understanding of the environmental, health and social aspects of becoming more plant-based.

- *The China Study* by Dr. T. Colin Campbell
- *How Not to Die* by Dr. Michael Greger and Gene Stone
- *Reverse the Signs of Ageing* by Dr. Nigma Talib
- *OMD: The Simple, Plant-Based Program to Save Your Health, Save Your Waistline, and Save the Planet* by Suzy Amis Cameron

- *Why We Love Dogs, Eat Pigs, and Wear Cows: An Introduction to Carnism* by Melanie Joy

- *The Flexitarian Diet* by Dawn Blatner

- *Spoon-Fed: Why Almost Everything We've Been Told about Food is Wrong* by Tim Spector

DOCUMENTARIES

A really quick and easy way to explore a hot topic. They are also a great talking point, so if there's someone you know who would like to – or should – watch one, there's a subject for everyone!

- Cowspiracy

- Seaspiracy

- Forks over Knives

- A Life on Our planet

- The Game Changers

- Rotten

- Sustainability

- What the Health

- Vegucated

- Health

WEBSITES AND SOCIAL MEDIA

These are the accounts we like to have on 'speed dial' for...

Recipe Inspiration

- deliciouslyella.com
- earthyandy.com
- thedoctorskitchen.com
- mynewroots.org
- veganricha.com
- minimalistbaker.com
- lazycatkitchen.com
- thegreenparent.co.uk
- mindbodygreen.com
- healthylivingjames.co.uk

Health Inspiration

- plantproof.com – a brilliant resource for understanding more about plant-based sources and quantities of macro and micro nutrients.

- nutritionstudies.org – for plant-based education (this is the certificate we graduated in), as well as exploring the latest research connecting lifestyle and disease.

- teamsherzai.com – husband and wife team, Drs. Sherzai offer practical advice on adapting your lifestyle for optimum brain health.

- drweil.com – an integrative medicine approach to health, our first port of call with any health concerns we need a natural solution for.

- theplantfedgut.com – for the science and practical advice on how a plant-based diet can help to optimise your gut health.

Recipe Index

Fruits & Vegetables	
Aubergine/Eggplant	Heartwarming Stew, Nut Crumb Aubergine Slices
Avocado	"Fauxghurt" Smoothie Bowl, Sweet Potato and Kale Salad, Tacos
Banana	Easy Cacao Overnight Oats, Warm Quinoa Oat Porridge
Bean Sprouts	All-in-a-Jar Noodles, Healthier-than-Take-Out Udon Noodles, Stir Fry Noodles
Beetroot	All-in-a-Jar Noodles, Poke Bowl
Blueberries	Easy Cacao Overnight Oats, "Fauxghurt" Smoothie Bowl, Warm Quinoa Oat Porridge
Bok Choy	Miso Soup, Stir Fry Noodles, Sweet Potato Fried Rice
Broccoli	Stir Fry Broccoli
Butternut Squash	Curried Butternut Squash
Carrots	Healthier-than-Take-Out Udon Noodles, Pav Bhaji, Poke Bowl, Rainbow Noodle Salad, Rice Paper Rolls, The Orange Soup
Coconut	All-in-a-Jar Noodles, Coconut Chia Pudding, Curried Butternut Squash, Easy Cacao Overnight Oats, Easy-Peasy Yellow Curry, Granola Munch
Courgette/Zucchini	Heartwarming Stew, Zucchini Burger

Cucumber	All-in-a-Jar Noodles, Couscous Salad and Harissa Tofu, Rice Paper Rolls
Garlic (including Garlic Powder)	All-in-a-Jar Noodles, Brown Chickpeas Pulao, Couscous Salad and Harissa Tofu, Curried Butternut Squash, Dry Chilli Tofu, Green Goodness Pasta, Healthier-than-Take-Out Udon Noodles, Heartwarming Stew, Home Style Bean Curry with Cumin Potatoes, Jackfruit Biryani, Leek Soup, Mushroom Soup, Nut Crumb Aubergine Slices, Plantier's Pesto, Roasted Red Bell Pepper and Cumin Hummus, Red Bell Pepper and Tomato Pasta, Stir Fry Broccoli, Sweet Potato Fried Rice, Tacos
Green Beans	Heartwarming Stew
Green Bell Pepper	Curried Butternut Squash, Home Style Bean Curry with Cumin Potatoes, Pav Bhaji, Rainbow Noodle Salad
Jackfruit	Jackfruit Biryani, Jackfruit Curry, Tacos
Kale	Sweet Potato and Kale Salad
Leek	Green Goodness Pasta, Leek Soup
Lemon	Bulgur Salad, Couscous Salad and Harissa Tofu, Mint and Coriander Chutney, Plantier's Pesto
Lettuce Leaves	Zucchini Burger
Lime	All-in-a-Jar Noodles, Curried Butternut Squash, Pav Bhaji, Rainbow Noodle Salad, Tacos
Mushrooms	All-in-a-Jar Noodles, Curried Butternut Squash, Miso Soup, Mushroom Soup, Tacos

Onion	Brown Chickpeas Pulao, Curried Butternut Squash, Dry Chilli Tofu, Easy-Peasy Yellow Curry, Healthier-than-Take-Out Udon Noodles, Heartwarming Stew, Home Style Bean Curry with Cumin Potatoes, Jackfruit Biryani, Jackfruit Curry, Masala Chickpeas with Spinach, Pav Bhaji, Savoury Chickpea Toast, Savoury Pancakes, Scrambled Tofu, Stir Fry Noodles, Sweet Potato Fried Rice, Spinach Dal, Tacos, Zucchini Burger
Orange	Rainbow Noodle Salad
Peas	Pav Bhaji
Pomegranate	Bulgur Salad
Potato	Curried Butternut Squash, Home Style Bean Curry with Cumin Potatoes, Pav Bhaji
Raspberries	Coconut Chia Pudding, Plantier's Bircher Muesli, Raspberry Compote
Red Bell Pepper	Easy-Peasy Yellow Curry, Rainbow Noodle Salad, Red Bell Pepper and Tomato Pasta, Roasted Red Bell Pepper and Cumin Hummus
Red Cabbage	Healthier-than-Take-Out Udon Noodles, Poke Bowl
Rocket/Arugula	Sweet Potato and Kale Salad
Spinach	Easy-Peasy Yellow Curry, Green Goodness Pasta, Masala Chickpeas with Spinach, Poke Bowl, Savoury Pancakes, Spinach Dal, Sweet Potato and Kale Salad
Spring Onions	All-in-a-Jar Noodles, Chilli Oil Silken Tofu, Curried Butternut Squash, Easy-Peasy Yellow Curry, Healthier-than-Take-Out Udon Noodles, Miso Soup, Rainbow Noodle Salad, Rice Paper Rolls, Stir Fry Noodles, Sweet Potato Fried Rice, Tacos, Zucchini Burger

Herbs & Spices	
Basil	Plantier's Pesto, Red Bell Pepper and Tomato Pasta
Bay Leaves	Brown Chickpeas Pulao, Jackfruit Biryani
Black Pepper	Bulgur Salad, Couscous Salad and Harissa Tofu, Leek Soup, Masala Chai, Mushroom Soup, Nut Crumb Aubergine Slices, Poke Bowl, Rainbow Noodle Salad, Stir Fry Noodles, Sweet Potato and Kale Salad, Tacos, The Orange Soup, Turmeric Latte
Cardamom	Brown Chickpeas Pulao, Jackfruit Biryani, Masala Chai, Sweet Squares
Chilli Flakes/Powder	Brown Chickpeas Pulao, Easy-Peasy Yellow Curry, Heart-warming Stew, Home Style Bean Curry with Cumin Potatoes, Jackfruit Biryani, Jackfruit Curry, Masala Chickpeas with Spinach, Savoury Chickpea Toast, Savoury Pancakes, Spinach Dal, Tacos
Cinnamon	Heartwarming Stew, Jackfruit Biryani, Masala Chai, Plantier's Bircher Muesli, Turmeric Latte
Cloves	Brown Chickpeas Pulao, Jackfruit Biryani, Masala Chai
Coriander	All-in-a-Jar Noodles, Curried Butternut Squash, Easy-Peasy Yellow Curry, Heartwarming Stew, Home Style Bean Curry with Cumin Potatoes, Jackfruit Curry, Masala Chickpeas with Spinach, Mint and Coriander Chutney, Pav Bhaji, Rainbow Noodle Salad, Rice Paper Rolls, Savoury Chickpea Toast, Savoury Pancakes, Spinach Dal, Tacos
Cumin	Brown Chickpeas Pulao, Heartwarming Stew, Jackfruit Biryani, Jackfruit Curry, Masala Chickpeas with Spinach, Roasted Red Pepper and Cumin Hummus, Savoury Chickpea Toast, Savoury Pancakes

*Glass Noodles are made from starch from a variety of different vegetables or legumes.

Sources

1 https://a0193a7b-04c0-45e2-b939-b1033d2f1ed3.filesusr.com/ugd/0c5d00_90935d6f-da344991a8fc2452eb112c83.pdf
2 https://www.who.int/dietphysicalactivity/publications/trs916/en/gsfao_global.pdf
3 https://www.abillion.com/
4 https://www.businessinsider.com/elite-athletes-who-are-vegan-and-what-made-them-switch-their-diet-2017–10?r=US&IR=T#hannah-teter-snowboarder-7
5 https://eatforum.org/eat-lancet-commission/eat-lancet-commission-summary-report/
6 https://www.theguardian.com/environment/2018/jul/19/rising-global-meat-consumption-will-devastate-environment
7 https://eatforum.org/eat-lancet-commission/eat-lancet-commission-summary-report/
8 https://www.un.org/development/desa/en/news/population/world-population-prospects-2019.html
9 https://eatforum.org/eat-lancet-commission/
10 https://eatforum.org/eat-lancet-commission/eat-lancet-commission-summary-report/
11 Poore, J., & Nemecek, T. (2018). Reducing food's environmental impacts through producers and consumers. Science, 360(6392), 987–992.
12 https://ourworldindata.org/food-ghg-emissions; https://www.wri.org/insights/interactive-chart-shows-changes-worlds-top-10-emitters
13 https://www.wri.org/insights/interactive-chart-shows-changes-worlds-top-10-emitters
14 Poore, J., & Nemecek, T. (2018). Reducing food's environmental impacts through producers and consumers. Science, 360(6392), 987–992.
15 Poore, J., & Nemecek, T. (2018). Reducing food's environmental impacts through producers and consumers. Science, 360(6392), 987–992.
16 https://ourworldindata.org/food-choice-vs-eating-local
17 Poore, J., & Nemecek, T. (2018). Reducing food's environmental impacts through producers and consumers. Science, 360(6392), 987–992.
18 Scarborough, Peter & Appleby, Paul & Mizdrak, Anja & Briggs, Adam & Travis, Ruth & Bradbury, Kathryn & Key, Timothy. (2014). Dietary greenhouse gas emissions of meat-eaters, fish-eaters, vegetarians and vegans in the UK. Climatic Change. 125. 10.1007/s10584–014–1169–1.
19 Scarborough, Peter & Appleby, Paul & Mizdrak, Anja & Briggs, Adam & Travis, Ruth & Bradbury, Kathryn & Key, Timothy. (2014). Dietary greenhouse gas emissions of meat-eaters, fish-eaters, vegetarians and vegans in the UK. Climatic Change. 125. 10.1007/s10584–014–1169–1.
20 Poore, J., & Nemecek, T. (2018). Reducing food's environmental impacts through producers

and consumers. Science, 360(6392), 987–992.

21   https://waterfootprint.org/en/

22   https://www.cowspiracy.com/

23   https://www.foei.org/

24   https://waterfootprint.org/en/

25   https://www.cowspiracy.com/

26   Poore, J., & Nemecek, T. (2018). Reducing food's environmental impacts through producers and consumers. Science, 360(6392), 987–992.

27   https://www.unccd.int/

28   https://www.peta.org/issues/animals-used-for-food/meat-environment/

29   https://www.cowspiracy.com/

30   https://awellfedworld.org/deforestation/

31   Qin, Y., Xiao, X., Wigneron, JP. et al. (2021) Carbon loss from forest degradation exceeds that from deforestation in the Brazilian Amazon. Nat. Clim. Chang.

32   https://www.ucsusa.org/resources/soybeans

33   https://awellfedworld.org/deforestation/

34   https://foodsource.org.uk/building-blocks/soy-food-feed-and-land-use-change

35   https://www.ourplanet.com/en/video/david-attenborough-a-life-on-our-planet-trailer/

36   Breitburg, Denise & Levin, Lisa & Oschlies, Andreas & Grégoire, Marilaure & Chavez, Francisco & Conley, Daniel & Garcon, V. & Gilbert, Denis & Gutiérrez, Dimitri & Isensee, Kirsten & Jacinto, Gil & Limburg, Karin & Montes, Ivonne & Naqvi, S.W.A. & Pitcher, Grant & Rabalais, N. & Roman, Michael & Rose, Kenneth & Seibel, Brad & Zhang, Jing. (2018). Declining oxygen in the global ocean and coastal waters. Science (New York, N.Y.). 359. 10.1126/science.aam7240.

37   https://www.bbc.com/news/science-environment-46459714

38   https://www.bbc.com/news/science-environment-46459714

39   Netflix investigative documentary series, Rotten, 2018

40   https://waterfootprint.org/en/about-us/news/news/grace-launches-new-water-foot-print-calculator/

41   Frankowska A, Jeswani HK, Azapagic A. Life cycle environmental impacts of fruit consumption in the UK. J Environ Manage. 2019 Oct 15

42   http://css.umich.edu/page/datafield

43   Robinson, B., Winans, K., Kendall, A. et al. A life cycle assessment of Agaricus bisporus mushroom production in the USA. Int J Life Cycle Assess 24, 456–467 (2019).

44   https://www.mushroomcouncil.com/mushroom-sustainability-story/

45   http://css.umich.edu/page/datafield

46   http://documents1.worldbank.org/curated/en/876071495118818649/pdf/115144-REVISED-20170530-Cocoa-final-updated.pdf

47   http://www.fao.org/news/story/en/item/40893/icode/

48   Convention on Biological Diversity (part of the UN), https://www.cbd.int/gbo5

49   https://www.who.int/news-room/fact-sheets/detail/noncommunicable-diseases

50   https://www.un.org/en/chronicle/article/lifestyle-diseases-economic-burden-health-ser-vices#:~:text=Lifestyle%20diseases%20share%20risk%20factors,metabolic%20syn-drome%2C%20chronic%20obstructive%20pulmonary

51   https://www.farmantibiotics.org/science-facts/antibiotic-infographs/human-vs-animal-anti-biotic-use-2/

52   https://www.fda.gov/animal-veterinary/cvm-updates/fda-releases-annual-summary-re-port-antimicrobials-sold-or-distributed-2019-use-food-producing

53   Spector, T. (2020), "Spoon-Fed: Why almost everything we've been told about food is wrong", Vintage Publishing, pp. 103.

54   https://www.who.int/news-room/fact-sheets/detail/antibiotic-resistance

55   https://www.theguardian.com/news/2018/mar/26/the-human-microbiome-why-our-mi-crobes-could-be-key-to-our-health

56   https://www.ncbi.nlm.nih.gov/pmc/articles/PMC2515351/

57   https://www.apa.org/monitor/2012/09/gut-feeling

58   https://www.frontiersin.org/articles/10.3389/fimmu.2018.02398/full#:~:text=About%20 50%25%20dopamine%20is%20produced,hepatic%20portal%20vein%20(6).

59   https://www.hsph.harvard.edu/nutritionsource/microbiome/

60   https://teamsherzai.com/

61   https://www.forbes.com/sites/nomanazish/2020/12/05/how-to-keep-your-brain-healthy-at-any-age-according-to-neurologists/?sh=3db73bd68121

62   https://theplantfedgut.com/

63   https://www.sciencedaily.com/releases/2018/05/180515092931.htm

64   https://www.nhs.uk/live-well/eat-well/how-to-get-more-fibre-into-your-diet/

65   Spector, T. (2020), "Spoon-Fed: Why almost everything we've been told about food is wrong", Vintage Publishing, pp. 55.

66   https://www.europarl.europa.eu/news/en/headlines/society/20180404STO00909/the-eu-s-organic-food-market-facts-and-rules-infographic

67   http://www.fao.org/organicag/oa-faq/oa-faq5/en/#:~:text=Certified%20organic%20prod-ucts%20are%20generally,for%20a%20number%20of%20reasons%3A&text=Marketing%20 and%20the%20distribution%20chain,because%20of%20relatively%20small%20volumes.

68   https://www.pan-uk.org/

69   https://www.ewg.org/

70   https://www.pan-uk.org/site/wp-content/uploads/Pesticides-in-our-food-FINAL.pdf

71   https://www.medscape.com/answers/184704-23259/what-is-the-worldwide-preva-lence-of-constipation

72   https://www.nhs.uk/live-well/eat-well/how-to-get-more-fibre-into-your-diet/

73   https://diet.mayoclinic.org/diet/eat/whole-grains-vs-regular-grains

74   https://www.nutrition.org.uk/nutritionscience/foodfacts/fortification.html?start=1

75   https://pubmed.ncbi.nlm.nih.gov/19709412/

76   https://www.hsph.harvard.edu/nutritionsource/legumes-pulses/#:~:text=A%20legume%20
        refers%20to%20any,the%20pod%20is%20the%20pulse.

77   https://pubmed.ncbi.nlm.nih.gov/22916805/

78   https://www.edisongroup.com/investment-themes/meat-alternatives-an-investment-analy-
        sis/28097/

79   https://www.edisongroup.com/investment-themes/meat-alternatives-an-investment-analy-
        sis/28097/

80   https://www.health.harvard.edu/staying-healthy/the-truth-about-fats-bad-and-good

81   https://www.healthline.com/nutrition/17-health-benefits-of-omega-3#TOC_TITLE_HDR_8

82   https://www.ncbi.nlm.nih.gov/pmc/articles/PMC6732875/

83   https://www.ncbi.nlm.nih.gov/pmc/articles/PMC2901047/

84   https://pubmed.ncbi.nlm.nih.gov/9619120/

85   https://pubmed.ncbi.nlm.nih.gov/20418184/

86   https://pubmed.ncbi.nlm.nih.gov/20594781/

87   https://www.health.harvard.edu/staying-healthy/the-truth-about-fats-bad-and-good

88   https://www.health.harvard.edu/staying-healthy/the-truth-about-fats-bad-and-good

89   https://www.diabetes.co.uk/food/trans-fats.html

90   https://www.forksoverknives.com/wellness/addictive-food-cheese-pizza/

91   https://www.forbes.com/sites/michaelpellmanrowland/2017/06/26/cheese-addic-
        tion/?sh=3fc58efd3583

92   https://www.worldometers.info/demographics/life-expectancy/

93   https://www.bluezones.com/

94   https://www.bluezones.com/recipes/food-guidelines/

95   https://www.bluezones.com/2016/11/power-9/

96   https://www.theguardian.com/environment/2019/jan/16/new-plant-focused-diet-would-
        transform-planets-future-say-scientists

97   https://www.nature.com/articles/s41586–018–0594–0.epdf

98   https://www.weforum.org/agenda/2018/11/want-to-save-the-world-become-a-flexitarian/

99   https://nutritionstudies.org/about/dr-t-colin-campbell/

100   https://www.forbes.com/sites/lanabandoim/2019/11/30/why-consumers-pre-
        fer-plant-based-instead-of-vegetarian-or-vegan-labels/?sh=7a47f0b87df3

101   https://vegconomist.com/interviews/abillionveg-socially-responsible-consumption-we-
        think-its-the-wave-of-the-future/

102   https://www.globaldata.com/

103   https://www.plantbasedfoods.org/marketplace/consumer-insights/

104   Pasi, Pohjolainen & Vinnari, Markus & Pekka, Jokinen. (2015). Consumers' perceived barriers to
        following a plant-based diet. British Food Journal. 117. 10.1108/BFJ-09–2013–0252.

105   https://www.forbes.com/sites/michaelpellmanrowland/2018/03/23/millennials-move-
        away-from-meat/

106   https://www.foodbusinessnews.net/articles/14408-holistic-nutrition-cuts-across-genera-

tions

107 https://impossiblefoods.com/blog/generational-trends-kids-in-the-kitchen

108 Joy, M. (2011). Why we love dogs, eat pigs, and wear cows: An introduction to carnism : the belief system that enables us to eat some animals and not others. Berkeley, Calif.: Conari.

109 https://www.ers.usda.gov/webdocs/publications/42432/15171_aib775f_1_.pdf?v=3014.2; Vanham, D. & Mak, Tsz & Gawlik, Bernd. (2016). Urban food consumption and associated water resources: The example of Dutch cities. Science of The Total Environment. 565. 232–239..

110 https://assets.website-files.com/5d823789d06ccc3a4ca208f6/5e52e1c7eba259f5e73ebe96_PV_Plant_Milk_Report_281019–1%20(2).pdf

111 Blatner, D. J. (2000). Flexitarian Diet. New York, USA: McGraw-Hill Professional Publishing.

112 https://eatforum.org/learn-and-discover/the-planetary-health-diet/

113 https://vegetarisk.dk/

114 Cameron, S.A. (2018). OMD: The Simple, Plant-Based Program to Save Your Health, Save Your Waistline, and Save the Planet. Atria Books

115 Cameron, S.A. (2018). OMD: The Simple, Plant-Based Program to Save Your Health, Save Your Waistline, and Save the Planet. Atria Books

116 https://omdfortheplanet.com/why-it-matters/planet/#:~:text=On%20average%2C%20just%20two%20football,person%20eating%20meat%20and%20dairy.&text=If%20everyone%20in%20the%20world,could%20be%20restored%20to%20forest.

117 https://www.macmillandictionary.com/dictionary/british/bliss-point

118 https://tonyschocolonely.com/int/en/our-story/our-mission

119 https://www.fairtrade.org.uk/

Lightning Source UK Ltd.
Milton Keynes UK
UKHW050330101121
393674UK00002B/99